PEPSI-COLA
COLLECTIBLES
(with prices)

> *For Additional*
> *Books Order*
> *From*
>
> **L-W Book Sales**
> Box 69
> Gas City, IN 46933
> **$14.95 + $1.25 Postage**

© 1990
Bill Vehling
Michael Hunt

PEPSI-COLA
COLLECTIBLES
(with prices)

© 1990
Bill Vehling
Michael Hunt

Published By
L-W Book Sales
Box 69
Gas City, IN 46933

TABLE OF CONTENTS

PREFACE

For two people who had been Pepsi Cola Collectors and dealers to be asked suddenly to become authors was quite a shock at first. However, we may be novices at writing books, but we certainly are not novices to Pepsi Cola collectibles.

The reasons why we decided to write a price guide on Pepsi Cola collectibles are threefold. First of all, to date, there has not been a single book written about Pepsi Cola memorabilia. Secondly, many dealers and collectors have asked us why we have not considered authoring a book about Pepsi Cola collectibles, since we have been collecting and dealing in Pepsi memorabilia for several years. Thirdly, the number of Pepsi collectors throughout the country is growing rapidly. And, with this rapid growth, we feel that there is a pressing demand for a comprehensive price guide on Pepsi Cola advertising.

This book is meant to be a general guide for pricing and dating Pepsi Cola collectibles, for both the collector and the dealer, whether beginner or advanced. Prices in this book are for near-mint items. Values are less for lesser conditioned pieces. Three factors determine the value of an item: <u>Condition</u> — condition is foremost for a serious collector, <u>Rarity</u> — it's the old principle of supply and demand, <u>Age</u> — the age of an item is the least critical of the three. Some items from the 1950's are more valuable than some items from the early 1900's.

We do not profess to be experts in the dating of these items. The pieces that have a specific date on them are noted as such. The other pieces are dated hopefully within ten years and are noted herein with the word "circa." Many pieces were produced and used for a longer time than ten years.

Just a word to the wise concerning "new or reproduction" items. Many, many different items in this category are being produced in astronomical amounts each year. Many disreputable dealers who deal in old advertising also are selling these worthless items as old. A word of caution to both the novice and advanced collector: **Beware of what you buy !!** If the dealer who sells the item will not guarantee that the item is old, then caution should be exercised.

We would certainly enjoy corresponding with fellow collectors and would appreciate hearing about any unique Pepsi Cola items you might have.

Please contact:

Bill Vehling
P.O. Box 41233
Indianapolis, IN 46241

Michael Hunt
P.O. Box 546
Brownsburg, IN 46112

Bill Vehling and Michael Hunt

ACKNOWLEDGEMENTS

We wish to express our sincere thanks to the people mentioned below without whose help this book would not have been possible.

Tony and Linda Solano
Bill and Roxanna Whitaker
Joe Kennedy
Bill Leerssen
Tim Smith
Neil Wood

With special thanks to . . .

Allan Petretti - *who provided us with numerous photos.*

Jay and Joan Millman - *two special friends who made their home and fine collection available.*

Nicholas Shepherd - *who allowed us to photograph his extensive collection.*

Marty Weinberger - *for providing us with photographs of many excellent pieces, including the great cover picture.*

Bob Stoddard - *founder of the Pepsi Cola Collectors Club.*

And most importantly to our wives Amy and Sharon, who work at regular jobs so that we can afford to do what we love, sell antique advertising, our heartfelt thanks. We love you both.

HELPFUL INFORMATION

Sizes: We have attempted to give accurate sizes whenever possible. Sizes are given as follows:

Width
Height
Depth

When only one dimension is given it refers to length.

Colors: Most Pepsi Cola items are basically colored red, white, and blue or combinations thereof. On items where other colors are predominant they are so indicated.

Grading: **Be conservative !** The owner of an item, whether he is a collector or a dealer, tends to over-grade his particular item. Don't fool yourself!

Main factors in determining condition:
Metal items - fading or discoloration of paint, chips, scratches, dents, or rust.
Paper or cardboard items - tears, waterspotting, or other discoloration.
China or glass items - chips or cracks.

For all pieces in general be sure they have no missing parts and have not been retouched. Restoration, if done properly, in most cases will make the item appear more presentable. However, a piece that has been restored is still not "original". It should be left up to the buyer and/or owner as to whether he prefers the piece "original" or restored.

For those who would like to join an organization that deals specifically with the collecting of Pepsi Cola memorabilia, please write to:

Pepsi-Cola Collectors Club
P.O. Box 1275
Covina, CA 91722

Membership in the club includes a very informative newsletter and the opportunity to buy from and sell Pepsi Cola memorabilia to other members of the club.

ABOUT THE AUTHORS

Michael Hunt is a lifelong resident of Indiana. In 1968 he started as a general line antique dealer; in 1970 he began collecting antique advertising, specializing in it as of 1972. He travels extensively throughout the year buying and selling.

Shortly after his marriage five years ago, he gave up steady employment and made a long-time wish a reality by becoming a full-time dealer. His wife Sharon, who was bitten by the "antique bug" shortly after they met, also enjoys the antique business and collecting.

The Hunts collect Pepsi-Cola memorabilia, plus a wide range of advertising items.

Mr. Hunt is a member of the Pepsi-Cola Collectors Club and the Tin Container Collectors Association.

Bill Vehling is a lifelong resident of Indianapolis, Indiana. He is a graduate of Indiana University and was an employee of General Motors for fourteen years. However, his love of the antique business won out and for the past eight years he has been a full-time dealer in antique advertising.

Mr. Vehling and his wife Amy have been avid collectors of antique advertising for over ten years. Their primary collecting has been in the field of soda water advertising.

Mr. Vehling is a member of the Pepsi-Cola Collectors Club, the Cola Clan, and the Tin Container Collectors Association.

Serving Trays

 # 1
Size: 11" x 14"
Date Circa.: 1900's
Value $1400

 # 3
Size: 11" x 14"
Date Circa.: 1900's
Value $700

 # 2
Size: 11" x 14"
Date Circa.: 1900's
Value $1200

Serving Trays

 # 5
Size: 14" x 11"
Description: Map
Date Circa.: 1930's
Value $250

 # 4
Size: 12" Diameter
Description: Bottling Company Tray
Date Circa.: 1930's
Value $325

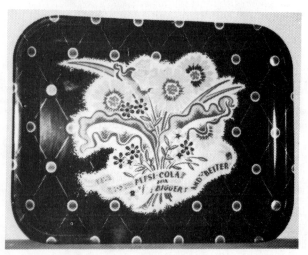

 # 7
Size: 14" x 11"
Description: Red, White, Blue
Date Circa.: 1930's
Value $45

 # 6
Size: 14" x 11"
Description: Black Background
Date Circa.: 1930's
Value $40

 # 8
Size: 10" x 14"
Date Circa.: 1940's
Value $250

 # 9
Size: 13"
Description: Red, White, Blue
Date Circa.: 1940's
Value $165

Serving Trays

 # 10
Size: 14" x 11"
Description: Red, White, Blue
Date Circa.: 1940's
Value $60

 # 11
Size: 12" Dia.
Description: Yellow
Date Circa.: 1950's
Value $35

 # 12
Size: 13" x 13"
Description: Red, White, Blue and Yellow
Date Circa.: 1950's
Value $45

 # 13
Size: 13" x 13"
Description: Red, White, Blue and Yellow
Date Circa.: 1950's
Value $45

 # 14
Size: 11" x 14"
Description: Product Tray
Date Circa.: 1950's
Value $50

 # 15
Size: 13"
Description: Product Tray
Date Circa.: 1950's
Value $55

Serving Trays

 # 16
Size: 12" Diameter
Description: Coney Island
Date Circa.: 1950's
Value $25

 # 17
Size: 12" Dia.
Description: Yellow and Blue
Date Circa.: 1960's
Value $45

 # 18
Size: 18" x 12"
Description: Plastic Cafeteria Tray
Date Circa.: 1960's
Value $20

 # 19
Size: 12" x 8"
Description: Rectangle with Ice
Date Circa.: 1970's
Value $20

 # 20
Size: 12" x 12"
Description: Flat Rim
Date Circa.: 1970's
Value $25

 # 21
Size: 9"
Description: Bicentennial
Date Circa.: 1976
Value $20

Tip Trays

 # 22
Size: 4½" x 6"
Date Circa.: 1908
Value $850

 # 23
Size: 4½" x 6"
Date Circa.: 1908
Value $800

 # 24
Size: 4½" x 6"
Date Circa.: 1908
Value $450

 # 25
Size: 6" Dia.
Description: Blue with White background
Date Circa.: 1906
Value $700

Tip Trays

 # 26
Size: 6" x 4"
Date Circa.: 1908
Value $450

 # 27
Size: 7" x 5"
Description: Advertising Reverse
Date Circa.: 1950's
Value $20

 # 28
Size: 7" x 5"
Description: Evervess - A Pepsi Product
Date Circa.: 1950's
Value $30

 # 29
Size: 7" x 5"
Description: Evervess - A Pepsi Product
Date Circa.: 1950's
Value $30

 # 30
Size: 7" Dia.
Description: Argentina Tip Tray
Date Circa.: 1960's
Value $30

Foreign Trays

 # 31
Size: 12" Diameter
Description: Chinese
Date Circa.: 1950's
Value $40

 # 32
Size: 12" Diameter
Description: Siamese
Date Circa.: 1950's
Value $40

 # 33
Size: 12" Dia.
Description: Arabic
Date Circa.: 1950's
Value $40

 # 34
Size: 12" Dia.
Description: Arabic
Date Circa.: 1960's
Value $40

 # 35
Size: 12" Dia.
Description: Arabic
Date Circa.: 1950's
Value $45

 # 36
Size: 13" x 13"
Description: Arabic
Date Circa.: 1950's
Value $40

Foreign Trays

 # 37
Size: 11" x 14"
Description: Arabic
Date Circa.: 1970's
Value $35

allegri ragazzi con...
PEPSI-COLA

 # 38
Size: 14" x 10"
Description: Spanish
Date Circa.: 1960's
Value $30

 # 39
Size: 13" Dia.
Description: Mexican
Date Circa.: 1960's
Value $25

 # 40
Size: 12"
Description: Mexican
Date Circa.: 1960's
Value $25

 # 41
Size: 12"
Description: Mexican
Date Circa.: 1960's
Value $25

 # 42
Size: 13" Dia.
Description: Mexican
Date Circa.: 1960's
Value $25

Ceramic & Other Holders

 # 43
Size: 3" x 3" x 6" (Cover Picture)
Description: Tin Straw Holder, 4-sided same
                graphics on each side, hinged to
                fold flat - Photo shows two sides
Date Circa.: 1909
Value $4000

Ceramic & Other Holders

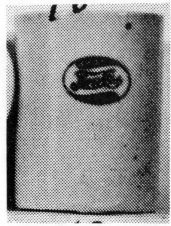

 # 46
Size: 2½" x 2½" x 2"
Description: Ceramic Menu
Holder
Date Circa.: 1940's
Value $300

 # 45
Size: 4" x 6"
Description: Ceramic Spoon
Holder
Date Circa.: 1940's
Value $375

 # 44
Size: 4" x 10"
Description: Ceramic Spoon
Holder
Date Circa.: 1940's
Value $450

 # 47
Size: 7" x 5" x 5"
Description: Ceramic Napkin
Holder
Date Circa.: 1940's
Value $400

 # 48
Size: 4½" x 3½" x 3½"
Description: Ceramic Straw
Holder
Date Circa.: 1940's
Value $325

 # 49
Size: 4"
Description: Ceramic Salt and
Pepper Shakers
Date Circa.: 1930's
Value $175

 # 50
Size: 5" x 3" x 1"
Description: Ceramic Pencil
Holder
Date Circa.: 1930's
Value $350

Ceramic & Other Holders

 # 51
Size: 24" x 18"
Description: Tin Bag Holder
Date Circa: 1930's
Value $600

 # 52
Size: 36" x 18"
Description: Tin Bag Holder
Date Circa.: 1940's
Value $375

 # 53
Size: 16" x 22"
Description: Tin String Holder
Date Circa.: 1930's
Value $450

 # 54
Size: 9" x 6" x 4"
Description: Metal Napkin Holder
Date Circa.: 1940's
Value $250

Ceramic & Other Holders

 # 55
Size: 4" x 4" x 4"
Description: Chrome Strawholder
Date Circa.: 1940's
Value $225

 # 56
Size: 4" x 4" x 4"
Description: Chrome Strawholder
Date Circa.: 1930's
Value $200

 # 58
Size: 7" x 3"
Description: Plastic Tooth Pick Holder
Date Circa.: 1940's
Value $125

 # 57
Size: 3" x 5"
Description: Bakelite Cup Holder
Date Circa.: 1940's
Value $125

 # 60
Size: 3" x 9"
Description: Plastic Napkin Holder
Date Circa.: 1960's
Value $10

 # 59
Size: 6" x 9"
Description: Plastic Menu Holder
Date Circa.: 1960's
Value $10

Straw Boxes

 # 61
Size: 4" x 12" x 4"
Description: Cardboard
Date Circa.: 1930's
Value $150

 # 62
Size: 4" x 12" x 4"
Description: Cardboard
Date Circa.: 1940's
Value $135

 # 63
Size: 4" x 12" x 4"
Description: Cardboard
Date Circa.: 1940's
Value $135

Straw Boxes

 # 64
Size: 4" x 10" x 4"
Description: Cardboard
Date Circa.: 1940's
Value $110

 # 65
Size: 4" x 12" x 4"
Description: Cardboard
Date Circa.: 1950's
Value $90

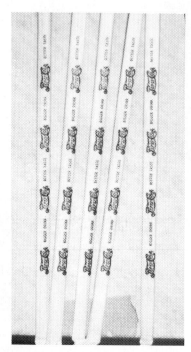

 # 66
Size: 12"
Description: Straws with marked wrappers
Date Circa.: 1940's
Value $15 each

Bottle Carriers

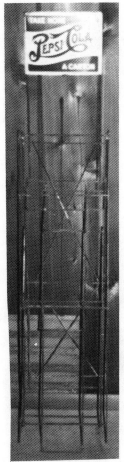

 # 67
Size: 51" High
Description: Metal Carton Rack
Date Circa.: 1940's
Value $165

 # 68
Size: 53" High
Description: Bottle Rack
Date Circa.: 1940's
Value $150

 # 69
38" High
Description: Bottle Rack
Date Circa.: 1940's
Value $175

#70
Size: 51"
Description: Bottle Rack
Date Circa.: 1930's
Value $225

#71
Size: 20 Bottle
Description: Metal
Date Circa.: 1930's
Value $165

#72
Size: 12 Bottle
Description: Metal
Date Circa.: 1930's
Value $150

Bottle Carriers

#73
Size: 24 Bottle
Description: Wooden
Date Circa.: 1930's
Value $55

#74
Size: 24 Bottle Case
Description: Wooden
Date Circa.: 1930's
Value $50

#75
Size: 8" x 11"
Wooden
Date Circa.: 1930's
Value $65

#76
Size: 8" x 10"
Description: Masonite
Date Circa.: 1940's
Value $100

#77
Size: 8" x 9"
Description: Wooden
Date Circa.: 1930's
Value $65

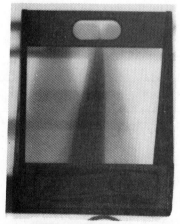

#78
Size: 8" x 11"
Description: Wooden
Date Circa.: 1930's
Value $65

#79
Size: 24 Bottles
Description: Wooden
Date Circa.: 1950's
Value $25

16

Bottle Carriers

 # 80
Size: 12 Bottle Carrier
Description: Metal
Date Circa.: 1930's
Value $115

 # 81
Size: 18" x 6" x 10"
Description: Metal Vendor's Carrier
Date Circa.: 1960's
Value $55

 # 82
Size: 20" x 12"
Description: Tin 12-Pack
Date Circa.: 1940's
Value $60

 # 83
Size: 10" x 12"
Description: Tin 6-Pack
Date Circa.: 1940's
Value $25

 # 84
Size: 10" x 12"
Description: Tin 6-Pack
Date Circa.: 1940's
Value $25

 # 85
Size: 10" x 12"
Description: Wire 6-Pack
Date Circa.: 1930's
Value $80

Bottle Carriers

 # 86
Size: 10" x 10"
Description: Tin Six Pack
Date Circa.: 1950's
Value $20

 # 87
Size: 10" x 10"
Description: Tin 6 Pack Yellow
Date Circa.: 1950's
Value $20

 # 88
Size: 10" x 12"
Description: Tin 6-Pack
Date Circa.: 1940's
Value $20

 # 89
Size: 2 Bottle
Description: Metal Carrier
Date Circa.: 1950's
Value $50

 # 90
Size: 6" x 4"
Description: 2 Bottle grocery cart carrier
Date Circa.: 1950's
Value $30

 # 91
Size: Single Bottle
Description: Metal Carrier
Date Circa.: 1950's
Value $50

Bottle Carriers

 # 92
Size: 12 Pack
Description: Heavy Cardboard
Date Circa.: 1950's
Value $40

 # 93
Size: 2 Bottle
Description: Cardboard Carrier
Date Circa.: 1950's
Value $30

 # 94
Size: 12 Pack
Description: Heavy Cardboard
Date Circa.: 1950's
Value $40

 # 95
Size: 12 Pack
Description: Heavy Cardboard
Date Circa.: 1950's
Value $40

 # 96
Size: 10" x 10"
Description: Cardboard 6-Pack
Date Circa.: 1950's
Value $10

 # 97
Size: 12" x 10"
Description: Cardboard 6-Pack Yellow
Date Circa.: 1950's
Value $15

Bottle Carriers

 # 98
Description: Cardboard Carrier
Date Circa.: 1930's
Value $35

 # 100
Size: 8" x 8"
Description: Cardboard 6-Pack
Date Circa.: 1940's
Value $40

 # 99
Size: 8" x 13"
Description: Cardboard 6-Pack
Date Circa.: 1940's
Value $45

 # 101
Size: 7¾" x 11"
Description: Cardboard Carrier
Date Circa.: 1930's
Value $35

 # 102
Size: 7¾" x 8¼"
Description: Cardboard Carrier
Date Circa.: 1940's
Value $40

 # 103
Size: 9" x 15"
Description: Cardboard 6-Pack
Date Circa.: 1930's
Value $40

Bottle Carriers

 # 104
Size: 8" x 10"
Description: Heavy Paper Bag
Date Circa.: 1930's
Value $50

 # 105
Size: 8" x 8"
Description: Heavy Paper Bag
Date Circa.: 1940's
Value $75

 # 106
Size: 8" x 8"
Description: Heavy Paper Bag
Date Circa.: 1940's
Value $75

 # 107
Size: 8" x 6"
Description: Heavy Paper Bag
Date Circa.: 1940's
Value $65

 # 108
Size: 8" x 8"
Description: Cardboard 6-Pack
Date Circa.: 1940's
Value $35

 # 109
Size: 8" x 8"
Description: Cardboard
Date Circa.: 1940's
Value $35

 # 110
Size: 4 Bottle
Description: Cardboard Carrier
Date Circa.: 1940's
Value $70

 # 111
Size: 24 Bottle
Description: Cardboard
Date Circa.: 1940's
Value $85

Bottle Carriers

 # 112
Size: 10" x 10"
Description: Cardboard 6-Pack
Date Circa.: 1950's
Value $10

 # 113
Size: 10" x 10"
Description: Cardboard 6-Pack
Date Circa.: 1950's
Value $10

 # 114
Description: Cloth 6 Bottle Carrier
Date Circa.: 1940's
Value $60

 # 115
Description: Cardboard Carrier
Date Circa.: 1930's
Value $45

 # 116
Description: Cardboard Carrier
Date Circa.: 1930's
Value $50

 # 117
Size: 6" x 4"
Description: 6 Pack Yellow
Date Circa.: 1960's
Value $30

Coolers

 # 118
Size: Double Case
Description: Glasscock Style
Date Circa.: 1930's
Value $800

 # 119
Size: Double Case
Description: Closed End Style
Date Circa.: 1930's
Value $675

 # 120
Size: 27" x 13" x 15"
Description: Metal Table Top
Date Circa.: 1930's
Value $500

 # 121
Size: 27" x 13" x 15"
Description: Metal Table top
Date Circa.: 1930's
Value $500

 # 122
Size: 16" x 18" x 16"
Description: Metal Table Top
Date Circa.: 1940's
Value $325

Coolers

 # 123
Size: 12" x 12" x 8"
Description: Metal Picnic
Date Circa.: 1940's
Value $175

 # 125
Size: 18" x 19" x 13"
Description: Metal
Date Circa.: 1940's
Value $110

 # 127
Size: 17" x 16" x 13"
Description: Metal-Chrome
Date Circa.: 1950's
Value $50

 # 124
Size: 17" x 16" x 13"
Description: Metal (Gray)
Date Circa.: 1940's
Value $110

 # 126
Size: 17" x 16" x 13"
Description: Metal Blue
Date Circa.: 1950's
Value $50

 # 128
Description: Metal Blue
Date Circa.: 1950's
Value $60

Radios

#129
Size: 28"
Description: Bake Lite with both original labels
Date Circa.: 1940's
Value $475

 # 130
Size: 28"
Description: Bake Lite (original bottom label)
Date Circa.: 1940's
Value $275

 # 131
Size: 28"
Description: Bake Lite with 2 New Labels
Date Circa.: 1940's
Value $175

 # 132
Size: 12" x 6" x 5"
Description: Plastic Machine
Date Circa.: 1960's
Value $325

 # 133
Size: 10" x 6" x 5"
Description: Plastic Cooler
Date Circa.: 1950's
Value $325

Radios

 # 134
Size: 12"
Description: Dispenser Radio
Date Circa.: 1960's
Value $200

 # 135
Size: 8"
Description: Machine Radio
Date Circa.: 1960's
Value $85

 # 136
Description: AM-FM Machine Radio
Date Recent
Value $20

 # 137
Description: Plastic Bottle Radio
Date Recent
Value $10

 # 138
Size: 12 oz.
Description: Can Radio
Date Circa.: 1960's
Value $20

 # 139
Size: 12 oz.
Description: Can Radio
Date Circa.: 1970's
Value $15

Clocks

 # 140
Size: 15" x 15"
Description: Glass Front Wood Frame
Date Circa.: 1930's
Value $175

 # 141
Size: 15" x 15"
Description: Glass Front Wood Frame
Date Circa.: 1930's
Value $175

 # 142
Size: 15" x 15"
Description: Glass Front Metal Frame
Date Circa.: 1940's
Value $145

 # 143
Size: 15" Dia.
Description: Glass Front Light Up
Date Circa: 1950's
Value $85

 # 144
Size: 15"
Description: Glass Front Lighted
Date Circa.: 1940's
Value $110

 # 145
Size: 12" Dia.
Description: Plastic Light Up
Date Circa.: 1950's
Value $110

 # 146
Size: 14" x 17"
Description: Plastic
Date Circa.: 1950's
Value $110

 # 147
Size: 15" Diameter
Description: Glass Front Light Up
Date Circa.: 1950's
Value $65

 # 148
Size: 15" x 15"
Description: Plastic Light Up
Date Circa.: 1960's
Value $75

Clocks

 # 149
Size: 30" Dia.
Description: Plastic Front Neon Tube
Date Circa.: 1950's
Value $500

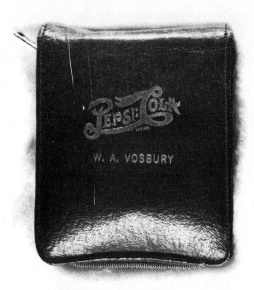

 # 150
Size: 3" x 4"
Description: Leather Cased Travel
Date Circa.: 1930's
Value $100

 # 151
Size: 10" x 8"
Description: Plastic Counter Clock
Date Circa.: 1960's
Value $40

 # 152
Size: 14" x 17"
Description: Plastic with Hood Light
Date Circa.: 1940's
Value $110

 # 153
Size: 12" x 18"
Description: Plastic Front
Date Circa.: 1960's
Value $40

 # 154
Size: 14" x 18"
Description: Plastic Light Up
Date Circa.: 1970's
Value $25

 # 155
Size: 14" x 6"
Description: Plastic Counter Clock
Date Circa.: 1970's
Value $25

Clocks

 # 156
Size: 18" x 12"
Description: Plastic Front Light up Yellow Background
Date Circa.: 1950's
Value $55

 # 157
Size: 16" x 16"
Description: Glass Front Lighted
Date Circa.: 1950's
Value $50

 # 158
Size: 15" Dia.
Description: Glass Front Lighted
Date Circa.: 1950's
Value $75

 # 159
Size: 17" Dia.
Description: Plastic Lighted
Date Circa.: 1950's
Value $100

 # 160
Size: 17" Dia.
Description: Metal
Date Circa.: 1960's
Value $125

 # 161
Size: 16" x 16"
Description: Glass Front Lighted
Date Circa.: 1960's
Value $40

Door Pushes

 # 162
Size: 30" x 3"
Description: Porcelain (Canadian)
Date Circa.: 1950's
Value $90

 # 163
Size: 30" x 3"
Description: Porcelain (Canadian)
Date Circa.: 1950's
Value $85

 # 164
Size: 30" x 3"
Description: Porcelain (Canadian)
Date Circa.: 1950's
Value $75

 # 165
Size: 30" x 3"
Description: Porcelain (Canadian)
Date Circa.: 1950's
Value $80

 # 171
Size: 3" x 10"
Description: Lithographed
Date Circa.: 1930's
Value $125

 # 166
Size: 30" x 3"
Description: Porcelain (Canadian)
Date Circa.: 1950's
Value $70

 # 167
Size: 30" x 3"
Description: Porcelain (Canadian)
Date Circa.: 1960's
Value $55

 # 168
Size: 30" x 3"
Description: Porcelain (French)
Date Circa.: 1950's
Value $85

 # 169
Size: 30" x 3"
Description: Porcelain (French)
Date Circa.: 1950's
Value $75

 # 170
Size: 30" x 3"
Description: Porcelain (French)
Date Circa.: 1950's
Value $75

 # 172
Size: 4" x 12"
Description: Tin Push Pla
Date Circa.: 1930's
Value $250

Door Pushes

 # 173
Size: 30" x 8"
Description: Push bar
Date Circa.: 1960's
Value $55

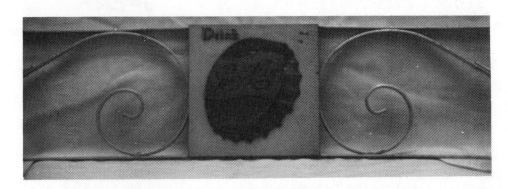

 # 174
Size: 30" x 8"
Description: Push bar
Date Circa.: 1950's
Value $50

 # 175
Size: 30" x 8"
Description: Push bar
Date Circa.: 1960's
Value $50

 # 176
Size: 30" x 8"
Description: Push bar
Date Circa.: 1960's
Value $55

 # 177
Size: 30" x 5"
Description: Metal
Date Circa.: 1960's
Value $30

 # 178
Size: 30" x 5"
Description: Push Bar
Date Circa.: 1960's
Value $25

Door Pushes

 # 179
Size: 4" x 12"
Description: Tin Plate with Bake Lite handle
Date Circa.: 1930's
Value $140

 # 180
Size: 3" x 12"
Description: Tin Plate with Bake Lite handle
Date Circa.: 1930's
Value $125

 # 183
Size: 4" x 12"
Description: Tin Push Plate Spanish Yellow
Date Circa.: 1930's
Value $115

 # 181
Size: 3" x 10"
Description: Tin Plate
Date Circa.: 1930's
Value $125

 # 182
Size: 3" x 10"
Description: Tin Push Plate
Date Circa.: 1930's
Value $125

Thermometers

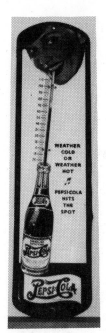

 # 184
Size: 7" x 27"
Description: Tin
Date Circa.: 1930's
Value $325

 # 185
Size: 7" x 27"
Description: Tin
Date Circa.: 1940's
Value $125

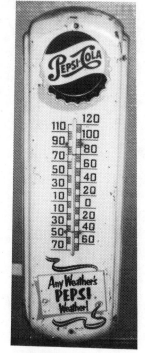

 # 186
Size: 7" x 27"
Description: Tin
Date Circa.: 1950's
Value $45

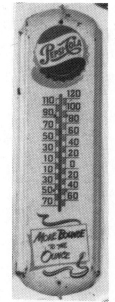

 # 187
Size: 7" x 27"
Description: Tin
Date Circa.: 1950's
Value $45

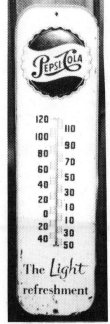

 # 188
Size: 7" x 27"
Description: Tin
Date Circa.: 1950's
Value $35

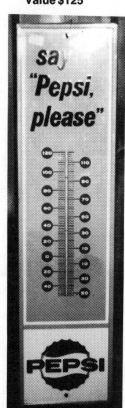

 # 189
Size: 7" x 27"
Description: Embossed Tin Yellow
Date Circa.: 1960's
Value $20

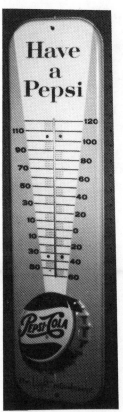

 # 190
Size: 7" x 27"
Description: Tin Yellow
Date Circa.: 1950's
Value $25

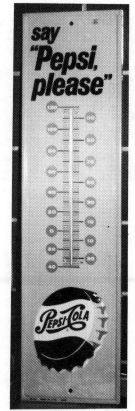

 # 191
Size: 7" x 27"
Description: Tin Yellow
Date Circa.: 1960
Value $15

Thermometers

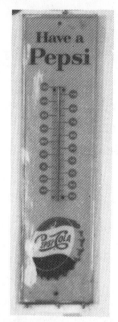

 # 192
Size: 6" x 16"
Description: Tin with original box
Date Circa.: 1940's
Value $175

 # 193
Size: 6" x 16"
Description: Tin
Date Circa.: 1940's
Value $125

 # 194
Size: 7" x 27"
Description: Tin Yellow
Date Circa.: 1960's
Value $20

 # 195
Size: 7" x 27"
Description: Tin
Date Circa.: 1970's
Value $15

 # 196
Size: 46" x 32"
Description: Glass Front
Date Circa.: 1970's
Value $60

 # 197
Size: 9" x 9"
Description: Tin/Cardboard Glass Front
Date Circa.: 1960's
Value $20

 # 198
Size: 10" x 10"
Description: Tin/Cardboard
Date Circa.: 1970's
Value $20

 # 199
Size: 12"
Description: Glass Front
Date Circa.: 1950's
Value $50

Menu Boards

 # 200
Size: 13" x 21"
Description: Cardboard with Tin Frame
Date Circa.: 1940's
Value $185

 # 201
Size: 20" x 30"
Description: Tin
Date Circa.: 1940's
Value $120

 # 202
Size: 20" x 30"
Description: Tin
Date Circa.: 1950's
Value $75

 # 203
Size: 15" x 23"
Description: Tin
Date Circa.: 1940's
Value $95

 # 204
Size: 20" x 30"
Description: Tin
Date Circa.: 1940's
Value $85

 # 205
Size: 20" x 30"
Description: Tin
Date Circa.: 1940's
Value $75

Menu Boards

 # 206
Size: 19" x 28"
Description: Tin
Date Circa.: 1930's
Value $110

 # 207
Size: 19" x 28"
Description: Tin
Date Circa.: 1930's
Value $85

 # 208
Size: 19" x 28"
Description: Tin French
Date Circa.: 1930's
Value $85

 # 209
Size: 19" x 30"
Description: Tin
Date Circa.: 1930's
Value $85

Menu Boards

 # 210
Size: 20" x 27"
Description: Tin
Date Circa.: 1950's
Value $50

 # 211
Size: 20" x 30"
Description: Tin
Date Circa.: 1950's
Value $50

 # 212
Size: 20" x 30"
Description: Tin
Date Circa.: 1960's
Value $35

 # 213
Size: 20" x 30"
Description: Tin
Date Circa.: 1950's
Value $30

 # 214
Size: 20" x 30"
Description: Tin
Date Circa.: 1960's
Value $20

 # 215
Size: 20" x 30"
Description: Tin
Date Circa.: 1970's
Value $15

Menu Boards

 # 216
Size: 28" x 26"
Description: Wood
Date Circa.: 1930's
Value $250

 # 217
Size: 20" x 30"
Description: Tin Yellow
Date Circa.: 1950's
Value $30

 # 218
Size: 20" x 30"
Description: Tin
Date Circa.: 1960's
Value $20

 # 219
Size: 27" x 39"
Description: Embossed Tin
Date Circa.: 1960's
Value $20

Tin Signs

 # 220
Size: 26" x 16"
Description: Embossed Green-Yellow
Date Circa.: 1900's
Value $1600

 # 222
Size: 15" x 6½"
Description: Embossed Green
Date Circa.: 1910
Value $550

 # 221
Size: 13" x 39"
Description: Embossed Green Background
Date Circa.: 1910
Value $1250

 # 223
Size: 28" x 19"
Description: Green and Yellow
Date Circa.: 1910's
Value $450

 # 224
Size: 28" x 10"
Description: Yellow and Black
Date Circa.: 1910's
Value $225

 # 225
Size: 12 x 3
Description: Yellow and Black
Date Circa.: 1910
Value $135

Tin Signs

 # 226
Size: 21" x 4"
Description: Embossed
Date Circa.: 1930's
Value $275

 # 227
Size: 56" x 31"
Description: Heavy Tin
Date Circa.: 1930's
Value $250

 # 228
Size: 12" x 45"
Description: Die Cut
Date Circa.: 1930's
Value $300

 # 229
Size: 41" x 51"
Description: Die Cut
Date Circa.: 1940's
Value $175

 # 230
Size: 27" x 18 1/2"
Date Circa.: 1940's
Value $165

Tin Signs

 # 231
Size: 40" x 12"
Description: Embossed
Date Circa.: 1930's
Value $200

 # 232
Size: 30" x 10"
Description: Embossed
Date Circa.: 1930's
Value $165

 # 234
Size: 28" x 12"
Description: Red, White, and Blue
Date Circa.: 1940's
Value $145

 # 235
Size: 54" x 18"
Date Circa.: 1930's
Value $180

 # 233
Size: 16" x 52"
Description: Red, White, and Blue
Date Circa.: 1930's
Value $275

 # 236
Size: 16" x 46"
Description: Heavy Tin
Date Circa.: 1930's
Value $225

Tin Signs

 # 237
Size: 24" x 14"
Description: Embossed, Wood Frame
Date Circa.: 1920's
Value $250

 # 238
Size: 28" x 20"
Description: Canadian Red, Blue and Yellow
Date Circa.: 1930's
Value $265

 # 239
Size: 26" x 10"
Description: Heavy Tin
Date Circa.: 1940's
Value $150

 # 240
Size: 23" x 11½"
Description: Embossed with Wooden Frame
Date Circa.: 1930's
Value $300

 # 241
Size: 18" x 7"
Description: Embossed
Date Circa.: 1920's
Value $175

 # 242
Size: 10" x 29"
Description: Die Cut
Date Circa.: 1930's
Value $275

Tin Signs

 # 243
Size: 20" Dia.
Description: Flange 2 sided
Date Circa.: 1930's
Value $200

 # 244
Size: 15" x 10"
Description: Flange 2-sided
Date Circa.: 1940's
Value $140

 # 245
Size: 17" x 17"
Description: Flange 2-Sided
Date Circa.: 1940's
Value $185

 # 246
Size: 13" Dia.
Description: Embossed
Date Circa.: 1940's
Value $80

 # 248
Size: 6¼" x 4½"
Description: License Plate Sign
Date Circa.: 1930's
Value $165

 # 247
Size: 30" x 26"
Description: Embossed
Date Circa.: 1940's
Value $125

Tin Signs

 # 249
Size: 13" Dia.
Description: Embossed
Date Circa.: 1940's
Value $95

 # 253
Size: 14" x 52"
Description: Red, White and Blue
Date Circa.: 1940's
Value $165

 # 254
Size: 36" x 14"
Description: Embossed Aluminum
Date Circa.: 1940's
Value $175

 # 250
Size: 14" x 1"
Description: Shelf Edge Sign
Date Circa.: 1930's
Value $45

 # 251
Size: 31" x 27"
Description: Embossed
Date Circa.: 1940's
Value $125

 # 252
Size: 36" x 12"
Description: Tops
Date Circa.: 1940's
Value $115

 # 255
Size: 13" x 12"
Description: Rack Sign
Date Circa.: 1940's
Value $55

 # 256
Size: 18" x 7"
Description: Embossed Red and White
Date Circa.: 1920's
Value $175

Tin Signs

 # 257
Size: 28" x 12"
Description: Heavy Tin
Date Circa.: 1950's
Value $85

 # 258
Size: 12" x 12"
Description: Yellow Background
Date Circa.: 1950's
Value $35

 # 259
Size: 17" x 5"
Description: Rack Sign
Date Circa.: 1940's
Value $60

 # 260
Size: 15" x 10"
Description: Porcelain
Date Circa.: 1950's
Value $55

 # 261
Size: 54" x 20"
Date Circa.: 1950's
Value $90

 # 262
Size: 15" x 10"
Description: Rack Sign
Date Circa.: 1950's
Value $35

 # 263
Size: 30" x 10"
Description: Embossed
Date Circa.: 1950's
Value $75

 # 264
Size: 36" x 14"
Description: Embossed
Date Circa.: 1960's
Value $35

 # 265
Size: 18" x 6"
Description: Rack Sign
Date Circa.: 1950's
Value $40

 # 266
Size: 30" x 10"
Description: Yellow, Red, White, and Blue
Date Circa.: 1950's
Value $55

Tins Signs

 # 267
Size: 16" x 48"
Date Circa.: 1950's
Value $100

 # 268
Size: 16" x 40"
Description: School Crossing Sign
Date Circa.: 1970's
Value $90

 # 269
Size: 18" x 44"
Description: Yellow Background
Date Circa.: 1960's
Value $70

 # 270
Size: 16" x 48"
Description: Embossed
Date Circa.: 1960's
Value $60

 # 271
Size: 7" x 27"
Description: Mileage
Date Circa.: 1960's
Value $40

 # 272
Size: 9" x 12"
Description: Tin / Cardboard
Date Circa.: 1960's
Value $30

 # 273
Size: 13" x 10"
Description: Heavy Tin 2- Sided
Date Circa.: 1970's
Value $30

 # 274
Size: 11" x 9"
Description: Tin / Cardboard
Date Circa.: 1960
Value $25

 # 275
Size: 31" Dia.
Description: Embossed
Date Circa.: 1950's
Value $55

Tin Signs

276
Size: 8' x 5'
Description: Original 8 piece display sign from "The Dog House" Mt. Summit, Indiana. Very rare to find a complete display.
Date Circa.: 1930's
Value $1200

Tin Signs

 # 277
Size: 18" x 54"
Description: Embossed
Date Circa.: 1930's
Value $500

 # 279
Description: Die Cut
Date Circa.: 1930's
Value $375

 # 278
Size: 26" x 18"
Description: Embossed
Date Circa.: 1930's
Value $185

 # 280
Size: 14" x 5"
Description: Hammered Tin
Date Circa.: 1930's
Value $135

 # 281
Size: 20" x 14"
Description: Yellow, Orange, and Black
Date Circa.: 1930's
Value $300

Foreign Signs

 # 282
Size: 23" x 25"
Description: 3-D Cardboard French
Date Circa.: 1930's
Value $225

 # 283
Size: 24" x 20"
Description: French Tin
Date Circa.: 1940's
Value $85

 # 284
Size: 24" x 20"
Description: French Tin
Date Circa.: 1940's
Value $75

 # 285
Size: 54" x 20"
Description: Embossed French Tin
Date Circa.: 1930's
Value $300

 # 286
Size: 24" x 20"
Description: Embossed French Tin
Date Circa.: 1930's
Value $150

 # 287
Size: 28" x 11"
Description: Mexican Cardboard
Date Circa.: 1950's
Value $35

 # 288
Size: 29" x 11"
Description: Mexican Tin
Date Circa.: 1940's
Value $60

Cardboard Signs

 # 289
Size: 21" x 11"
Date Circa.: 1930's
Value $425

 # 290
Size: 28" x 11"
Date Circa.: 1940's
Value $125

 # 291
Size: 28" x 11"
Date Circa.: 1940's
Value $100

 # 292
Size: 28" x 11"
Date Circa.: 1940's
Value $175

 # 293
Size: 28" x 11"
Date Circa.: 1940's
Value $100

 # 294
Size: 28" x 11"
Date Circa.: 1940's
Value $110

 # 295
Size: 28" x 11"
Date Circa.: 1940's
Value $95

 # 296
Size: 28" x 11"
Date Circa.: 1940's
Value $125

Cardboard Signs

 # 297
Size: 28" x 11"
Date Circa.: 1930's
Value $350

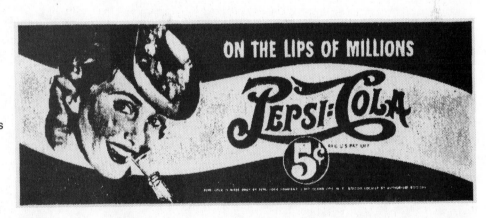

 # 298
Size: 28" x 11"
Date Circa.: 1930's
Value $350

 # 299
Size: 28" x 11"
Date Circa.: 1930's
Value $300

Cardboard Signs

 # 300
Size: 28" x 11"
Date Circa.: 1930's
Value $300

 # 301
Size: 28" x 11"
Date Circa.: 1930's
Value $300

 # 302
Size: 28" x 11"
Date Circa.: 1930's
Value $300

 # 303
Size: 21" x 11"
Date Circa.: 1930's
Value $225

Cardboard Signs

 # 304
Size: 28" x 11"
Description: W./Original Frame
Date Circa.: 1940's
Value $125

 # 305
Size: 28" x 11"
Description: Original Frame
Date Circa.: 1960's
Value $35

 # 306
Size: 28" x 11"
Date Circa.: 1950's
Value $35

 # 307
Size: 28" x 11"
Description: Original Frame
Date Circa.: 1950's
Value $35

 # 308
Size: 28" x 11"
Date Circa.: 1950's
Value $30

 # 309
28" x 11"
Description: Original Frame
Date Circa.: 1960's
Value $35

 # 310
Size: 28" x 11"
Description: Original Frame
Date Circa.: 1960's
Value $20

 # 311
Size: 28" x 11"
Description: Original Frame
Date Circa.: 1960's
Value $20

Cardboard Signs

 # 312
Size: 16" x 22"
Description: Paper
Date Circa.: 1900's
Value $1050

 # 313
Size: 25" x 31"
Description: Rolf Armstrong with Marked Wood Frame
Date: 1919
Value $700

Cardboard Signs

 # 314
Size: 25" x 34"
Description: Self Framed
Date Circa.: 1930's
Value $325

 # 315
Size: 24" x 31"
Description: Self Framed
Date Circa.: 1930's
Value $265

 # 316
Size: 25" x 34"
Description: Self Framed
Date Circa.: 1930's
Value $275

 # 317
Size: 25" x 34"
Description: Self Framed
Date Circa.: 1930's
Value $275

Cardboard Signs

 # 318
Size: 19" x 26"
Description: Self Framed
Date Circa.: 1940's
Value $265

 # 319
Size: 25" x 34"
Description: Self Framed
Date Circa.: 1930's
Value $210

 # 320
Size: 25" x 34"
Description: Self Framed
Date Circa.: 1930's
Value $200

 # 321
Size: 26" x 21"
Description: Self Framed
Date Circa.: 1940's
Value $150

Cardboard Signs

 # 322
Size: 28" x 21"
Description: Self Framed
Date Circa.: 1940's
Value $175

 # 323
Size: 26" x 20"
Description: Self Framed
Date Circa.: 1950's
Value $110

 # 324
Size: 18" x 26"
Description: Easel Back
Date Circa.: 1930's
Value $550

 # 325
Size: 36" x 24"
Description: Paper
Date Circa.: 1940's
Value $300

Cardboard Signs

 # 326
Size: 28" x 35"
Description: Poster
Date Circa.: 1940's
Value $175

 # 327
Size: 38" x 28"
Description: Poster
Date Circa.: 1940's
Value $120

 # 328
Size: 36" x 29"
Description: Poster
Date Circa.: 1940's
Value $125

 # 330
Size: 38" x 28"
Description: 38" x 28"
Date Circa.: 1940's
Value $135

 # 329
Size: 37" x 25"
Description: Poster
Date Circa.: 1940's
Value $125

 # 331
Size: 37" x 25"
Description: Poster
Date Circa.: 1940's
Value $80

Cardboard Signs

 # 332
Size: 38" x 28"
Description: Poster
Date Circa.: 1950's
Value $60

 # 333
Size: 38" x 28"
Description: Poster
Date Circa.: 1950's
Value $60

 # 334
Size: 38" x 28"
Description: Poster
Date Circa.: 1950's
Value $60

 # 335
Size: 38" x 28"
Description: Poster
Date Circa.: 1950's
Value $55

 # 336
Size: 38" x 28"
Description: Poster
Date Circa.: 1960's
Value $45

 # 337
Size: 54" x 40"
Description: Heavy Paper Poster
Date Circa.: 1950's
Value $135

 # 338
Size: 60" x 24"
Description: Heavy Paper
Date Circa.: 1940's
Value $165

 # 339
Size: 65" x 20"
Description: Heavy Paper
Date Circa.: 1950's
Value $85

Cardboard Signs

 # 340
Description: 7 Piece Pepsi and Pete back bar festoon
Date Circa.: 1930's
Value $850

 # 341
Size: 20" x 14"
Description: Die Cut Easel Back
Date Circa.: 1930's
Value $275

 # 342
Size: 21" x 14"
Description: Die Cut 2 sided
Date Circa.: 1930's
Value $250

 # 343
Size: 10" x 14"
Description: Die Cut Easel Back
Date Circa.: 1930's
Value $200

 # 344
Size: 21" x 14"
Description: Die Cut 2 sided
Date Circa.: 1930's
Value $250

Cardboard Signs

 # 345
Size: 14" x 14"
Description: Die Cut Bottle Display
Date Circa.: 1930's
Value $275

 # 346
Size: 14" x 14"
Description: 2 sided Die Cut
Date Circa.: 1930's
Value $95

 # 347
Size: 10" x 10"
Description: Die Cut Easel Back
Date Circa.: 1930's
Value $125

348
ze: 4" x 10"
escription: Figural Paper Sign (2-Sided)
ate Circa.: 1930's
alue $95

 # 349
Size: 8" x 5"
Description: Hanging Sign
Date Circa.: 1940's
Value $125

 # 350
Size: 12" x 12"
Description: 2 Sided Die Cut
Date Circa.: 1930's
Value $95

 # 351
Size: 12" x 6"
Description: Hanger
Date Circa.: 1940's
Value $185

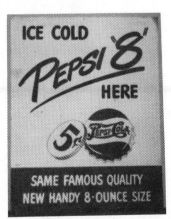

 # 352
Size: 11" x 14"
Description: Easel Back
Date Circa.: 1940's
Value $50

 # 353
Size: 6" x 12"
Description: Easel Back
Date Circa.: 1940's
Value $45

Cardboard Signs

 # 354
Size: 13" x 30"
Description: 2-Sided (Baseball - Football) Scoreboard
Date Circa.: 1930's
Value $275

 # 356
Size: 13 1/2" x 5 1/2"
Date Circa.: 1910
Value $300

 # 355
Size: 12" x 18"
Description: Paper Window Decal
Date Circa.: 1940's
Value $275

 # 357
Size: 18" x 15"
Description: Easel Back
Date Circa.: 1930's
Value $300

 # 358
Size: 23" x 25"
Description: 3-D Easel Back
Date Circa.: 1930's
Value $325

Cardboard Signs

 # 359
Size: 26" x 36"
Description: Die Cut Easel Back
Date Circa.: 1940's
Value $285

 # 360
Size: 5" x 18"
Description: Bottle Holder Foil Covered
Date Circa.: 1930's
Value $75

 # 361
Size: 20" x 28"
Description: Heavy Paper
Date Circa.: 1940's
Value $125

 # 363
Size: 16" x 26"
Description: Die Cut
Easel Back
Date Circa.: 1940's
Value $165

 # 364
Size: 8" x 18"
Description: Die Cut
Easel Back
Date Circa.: 1940's
Value $250

 # 362
Size: 16" x 24"
Description: Paper
Date Circa.: 1940's
Value $285

 # 365
Size: 8" x 16"
Date Circa.: 1930's
Value $150

 # 367
Size: 6" x 8"
Description: Bottle Topper
Date Circa.: 1940's
Value $135

 # 366
Size: 8" x 16"
Date Circa.: 1930's
Value $150

 # 368
Size: 12" Dia.
Description: Petty Art
Date Circa.: 1940's
Value $125

Cardboard Signs

 # 369
Size: 36" x 16"
Description: 3-D
Window Display
Date Circa.: 1940's
Value $300

 # 371
Size: 14" x 37"
Description: Die Cut
Date Circa.: 1940's
Value $285

 # 370
Size: 12" x 10"
Description: Window Decal
Date Circa.: 1940's
Value $110

 # 373
Size: 12" x 10"
Description: Paper Window Decal
Date Circa.: 1940's
Value $110

 # 372
Size: 4" x 7"
Description: Die Cut Paper
Date Circa.: 1940's
Value $90

 # 374
Size: 5" Diameter
Description: Cardboard Fan Pull
Date Circa.: 1940's
Value $45

 # 375
Size: 11" x 6"
Description: Paper Scale Model Logo
Date Circa.: 1940's
Value $50

Cardboard Signs

 # 376
Size: 16" x 20"
Description: 3-D Easel Back
Date Circa.: 1950's
Value $45

 # 377
Size: 17" x 24"
Description: Die Cut
Date Circa.: 1950's
Value $65

 # 378
Size: 16" x 20"
Description: Die Cut Easel Back
Date Circa.: 1950's
Value $55

 # 379
Size: 15" x 20"
Description: Die Cut
Date Circa.: 1950's
Value $35

 # 380
Size: 12" x 6"
Description: Foil Covered
Date Circa.: 1960's
Value $25

 # 381
Size: 5" x 8"
Description: Foil Covered Easel Back
Date Circa.: 1950's
Value $25

 # 382
Size: 12" x 12"
Description: Die Cut
Date Circa.: 1950's
Value $30

 # 383
Size: 36" x 20"
Description: Tri Fold Window Display
Date Circa.: 1950's
Value $110

Cardboard Signs

 # 384
Size: 19" x 22"
Description: Easel Back
Date Circa.: 1950's
Value $30

 # 386
Size: 14" x 20"
Description: Cardboard Football Schedule
Date 1969
Value $25

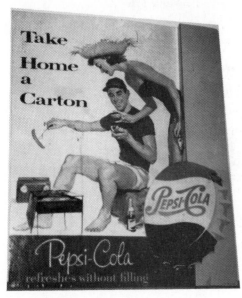

 # 385
Size: 17 1/2" x 20 1/2"
Description: 3-D Easel Back
Date Circa.: 1950's
Value $35

 # 387
Size: 18" x 21"
Description: 3-D Easel Back
Date Circa.: 1950's
Value $35

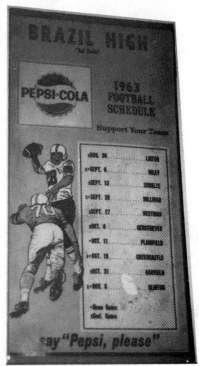

 # 388
Size: 14" x 20"
Description: Cardboard Football Schedule
Date 1963
Value $25

Cardboard Signs

 # 389
Size: 6" x 4"
Description: Embossed (Green Background)
Date Circa.: 1910's
Value $275

 # 390
Size: 15" x 21"
Description: Easel Back
Date Circa.: 1930's
Value $185

 # 391
Size: 8" x 5"
Description: Paper Window Decal
Date Circa.: 1940's
Value $95

Santas

 # 392
Size: 4 Foot
Description: Cardboard Easel Back
Date Circa.: 1960's
Value $55

 # 393
Size: 18" High
Description: Cardboard Easel Back
Date Circa.: 1950's
Value $45

 # 394
Size: 14" high
Description: Cardboard Easel Back
Date Circa.: 1940's
Value $100

 # 396
Size: 18" High
Description: Cardboard Easel Back
Date Circa.: 1960's
Value $35

 # 395
Size: 18" High
Description: Cardboard Easel Back
Date Circa.: 1960's
Value $35

 # 397
Size: 30"
Description: Plastic 3-D
By Norman Rockwell
Date Circa.: 1970's
Value $30

 # 398
Size: 19" High
Description: Cardboard
By Norman Rockwell
Date Circa.: 1960's
Value $35

Celluloid Signs

 # 399
Size: 9" Diameter
Description: Celluloid / Tin
Date Circa.: 1940's
Value $110

 # 400
Size: 9" Diameter
Description: Celluloid / Tin
Date Circa.: 1930's
 Value $125

 # 401
Size: 9" Diameter
Description: Celluloid / Tin
Date Circa.: 1940's
Value $85

 # 402
Size: 12" Diameter
Description: Celluloid / Tin
Date Circa.: 1950's
Value $65

 # 403
 Size: 9" Diameter
Description: Celluloid Over Tin
Date 1950
Value $40

 # 404
Size: 12" x 8"
Description: Celluloid / Tin
Date Circa.: 1960's
Value $60

Celluloid Signs

 # 405
Size: 5" x 13"
Description: Celluloid / Tin
Date Circa.: 1930's
Value $400

 # 406
Size: 8" x 12"
Description: Celluloid / Tin
Date 1960's
Value $65

 # 407
Size: 8" x 12"
Description: Celluloid / Tin
Date Circa.: 1950's
Value $45

 # 408
Size: 8" x 12"
Description: Celluloid / Tin
Date Circa.: 1950's
Value $75

 # 409
Size: 15" x 15"
Description: Celluloid / Wood 2 sided
Date Circa.: 1930's
Value $265

 # 410
Size: 8" x 12"
Description: Celluloid / Tin
Date Circa.: 1960's
Value $55

Glass Signs

411
Size: 10" x 12"
Description: Chain Edge, (Miss Pepsi Cola)
Date Circa.: 1900's
Value $6000

Glass Signs

 # 412
Size: 14" x 10"
Description: Mirror with wood frame
Date Circa.: 1930's
Value $350

 # 413
Size: 18" x 9"
Description: Reverse on Glass Wood Frame
Date Circa.: 1930's
Value $175

 # 414
Size: 7" x 4"
Description: Paper Under Glass
Date Circa.: 1930's
Value $250

 # 415
Size: 10" x 12"
Description: Mirror
Date Circa.: 1950's
Value $55

 # 416
Size: 10" x 10"
Description: Mirror Sign
Date Circa.: 1950's
Value $125

 # 417
Size: 8" x 14"
Description: Mirror
Date Circa.: 1950's
Value $65

 # 418
Size: 6" x 14"
Description: Mirror
Date Circa.: 1950's
Value $85

 # 419
Size: 8" x 10"
Description: Parking Meter Topper
Date Circa.: 1940's
Value $200

Light Up Signs

 # 420
Size: 20 1/2" x 10" x 7 1/2"
Description: Plastic Front Metal Frame Revolving Cylinders
Date Circa.: 1950's
Value $275

 # 421
Size: 18" x 12"
Description: Plastic Revolving
Date Circa.: 1960's
Value $225

 # 423
Size: 14" x 14"
Description: Plastic
Date Circa.: 1960's
Value $25

 # 424
Size: 28" x 46"
Description: Plastic 3-D
Date Recent
Value $135

 # 422
Size: 10" x 12"
Description: Revolving
Date Circa.: 1970's
Value $35

 # 425
Size: 19" x 9"
Description: Plastic Front
Date Circa.: 1940's
Value $375

 # 426
Size: 16" x 12"
Description: Plastic
Date Circa.: 1950's
Value $110

 # 427
Size: 12" x 3" x 3"
Description: Hotel Reading Light
Date Circa.: 1940's
Value $85

Plastic Signs

 # 428
Size: 9" x 12"
Description: 3-D Stand-up
Date Circa.: 1940's
Value $125

 # 429
Size: 13" x 10"
Description: 2-Sided
Date Circa.: 1970's
Value $25

 # 430
Size: 13" x 10"
Description: 2-Sided
Date Circa.: 1960's
Value $30

 # 431
Size: 12" Dia.
Description: Flasher 2-Slogans
Date Circa.: 1950's
Value $45

 # 432
Description: Large Display 6 pack plastic and cardboa
Date Circa.: 1960's
Value $110

Plastic Signs

 # 433
Size: 20" x 10"
Description: 3-D, Over Masonite
Date Circa.: 1940's
Value $125

 # 434
Size: 6" x 10"
Description: Embossed
Date Circa.: 1960's
Value $25

 # 435
Size: 9" x 9"
Description: Cut Out
Date Circa.: 1950's
Value $20

 # 436
Size: 12" x 10"
Description: Embossed 3-D
Date Circa.: 1960's
Value $35

 # 437
Size: 3" Dia.
Description: Fan Hanger (CDBD Insert)
Date Circa.: 1940's
Value $35

 # 438
Size: 3" Dia.
Description: Fan Hanger (CDBD Insert)
Date Circa.: 1940's
Value $35

Wooden Signs

 # 439
Size: 11" x 8"
Description: Composition
Date Circa.: 1940's
Value $125

 # 440
Size: 10" x 7"
Description: Composition Cash Register Topper
           Describes Counterfeit Money on Back
Date Circa.: 1930's
Value $165

 # 441
Size: 12" Dia.
Description: Masonite 2-sided flange
Date Circa.: 1940's
Value $175

 # 442
Size: 23" x 18"
Description: Masonite
Date Circa.: 1950's
Value $35

Syrup Containers

 # 443
Size: 5 Gallon
Description: Metal
Date Circa.: 1930's
Value $60

 # 444
Size: 5 Gal.
Description: Metal
Date Circa.: 1940's
Value $55

 # 446
Size: 5 Gal.
Description: Metal
Date Circa.: 1930's
Value $70

 # 445
Size: 5 Gal.
Description: Tin Silver & Red
Date Circa.: 1940's
Value $85

 # 448
Size: 5 Gal.
Description: Wood Barrel with paper label
Date Circa.: 1920's
Value $200

 # 447
Size: 5 Gal.
Description: Wooden Barrell with paper labels
Date Circa.: 1920's
Value $200

Syrup Containers

 # 449
Size: 1 Gal.
Description: Embossed Glass Jug
Date Circa.: 1930's
Value $275

450
Size: 1 Gal.
Description: Glass Jug
Date Circa.: 1960's
Value $25

 # 451
Size: 1 Gal.
Description: Glass Jug
Date Circa.: 1960's
Value $25

 # 452
Size: 12 oz.
Description: Glass Bottle
Date Circa.: 1940's
Value $20

 # 453
Size: 1 Gal.
Description: All Glass Jug
Date Circa.: 1950's
Value $50

 # 454
Size: 1 Gal.
Description: Glass Jug with paper label
Date Circa.: 1950's
Value $30

 # 455
Size: 1 Gal.
Description: Glass Jug with paper
Date Circa.: 1950's
Value $45

 # 456
Size: 1 Gal.
Description: Tin
Date Circa.: 1940's
Value $80

 # 457
Size: 1 Gal.
Description: Tin
Date Circa.: 1950's
Value $45

 # 458
Size: 1 Gal.
Description: Tin
Date Circa.: 1950's
Value $50

Syrup Dispensers and Tap Knobs

 # 459
Size: 8" x 24"
Description: China
Date Circa.: 1900's
Value $6500

Syrup Dispensers and Tap Knobs

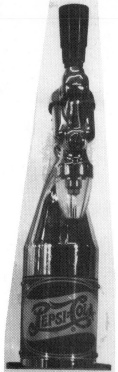

 # 460
Size: 18" High
Description: Heavy Chrome
Date Circa.: 1940's
Value $425

 # 461
Size: 1 Gal.
Description: Tin and Metal
Date Circa.: 1940's
Value $265

 # 462
Size: 17"
Description: Celluloid and Metal Musical Tap
Date Circa.: 1940's
Value $195

 # 463
Description: Metal
Date Circa.: 1950's
Value $90

 # 464
Size: 1 3/4" x 2 1/2"
Description: Plastic Tap Knob (Tin Insert)
Date Circa.: 1930's
Value $75

 # 465
Size: 4"
Description: Celluloid & Metal Musical Tap
Date Circa.: 1940's
Value $165

 # 466
Description: Metal
Date Circa.: 1950's
Value $125

 # 467
Description: Chrome
Date Circa.: 1940's
Value $245

Glasses and Cups

 # 468
Size: 12 oz.
Description: Paper Cup
Date Circa.: 1930's
Value $50

 # 469
Size: 12 oz.
Description: Paper Cup
Date Circa.: 1930's
Value $50

 # 470
Size: 10 oz.
Description: Paper Cup
Date Circa.: 1930's
Value $35

 # 471
Size: 10 oz.
Description: Paper Cup
Date Circa.: 1960's
Value $5

 # 472
Size: 12 oz.
Description: Paper Cup
Date Circa.: 1960's
Value $5

 # 473
Size: 12 oz.
Description: ACL
Date Circa.: 1960's
Value $10

 # 474
Size: 12 oz.
Description: ACL
No syrup line
Date Circa.: 1950's
Value $15

 # 475
Size: 10 oz
Description: ACL
No syrup line
Date Circa.: 1940's
Value $20

 # 476
Size: 10 oz.
Description: ACL
with syrup line
Date Circa.: 1940's
Value $20

 # 477
Size: 10 oz.
Description: ACL
with syrup line
Date Circa.: 1940's
Value $35

 # 478
Size: 10 oz.
Description: Paper Cup
Date Circa.: 1960's
Value $5

 # 479
Size: 12 Glasses
Description: Cardboard Box
For 10 oz Glasses
Date Circa.: 1940's
Value $50

 # 480
Size: 10 oz.
Description: Paper Cup
Date Circa.: 1970's
Value $5

Bottles

 # 481
Size: 6 oz.
Description: Hutchinson Bottle, Pensacola, Fl.
Date Circa.: 1905
Value $375

 # 482
Size: 36 oz.
Description: ACL Seltzer
Date Circa.: 1930's
Value $350

 # 483
Size: 20"
Description: Display Bottle
Date Circa.: 1960's
Value $200

 # 484
Size: 7 oz.
Description: Amber Embossed
Date Circa.: 1906
Value $125

 # 485
Size: 7 oz.
Description: Green Embossed Drum
Date Circa.: 1910's
Value $90

 # 486
Size: 7 oz.
Description: Green Embossed
Date Circa.: 1910's
Value $75

 # 487
7 oz.
Description: Purple Embossed
Date Circa.: 1910's
Value $80

Bottles

 # 489
Size: 7 oz.
Description: Aqua Embossed
Date Circa.: 1910's
Value $65

 # 490
Size: 7 oz.
Description: Aqua Embossed
Date Circa.: 1910's
Value $60

 # 491
Size: 7 oz.
Description: Green Embossed
with original paper label
Date Circa.: 1910's
Value $200

 # 492
Size: 7 oz.
Description: Green Embossed
Date Circa.: 1910's
Value $60

8
: 7 oz.
cription: Aqua Embossed
Circa.: 1910's
e $60

93
e: 7 oz.
scription: Clear Embossed
e Circa.: 1910's
lue $60

 # 494
Size: 12 oz.
Description: Green with paper labels
Date Circa.: 1930's
Value $55

 # 495
Size: 12 oz.
Description: Green with paper labels
Date Circa.: 1930's
Value $60

 # 496
Size: 12 oz.
Description: Amber Paper Labels
Date Circa.: 1930's
Value $70

 # 497
Size: 12 oz.
Description: Clear with paper label
Date Circa.: 1930's
Value $30

Bottles

 # 498
Size: 24 oz.
Description: Clear with paper label
Date Circa.: 1950's
Value $50

 # 499
Size: 12 oz.
Description: ACL Red and White
Date Circa.: 1940's
Value $10

 # 500
Size: 12 oz.
Description: ACL red white and blue
Date Circa.: 1940's
Value $10

 # 501
Size: 12 oz.
Description: ACL
Date Circa.: 1940's
Value $15

 # 502
Size: 12 oz.
Description: ACL
Date Circa.: 1950's
Value $5

 # 503
Size: 12 oz.
Description: Russian Paper Labels
Date Circa.: 1960's
Value $20

 # 504
Size: 8 oz.
Description: Clear Foil Label French
Date Circa.: 1960's
Value $10

 # 505
Size: 12 oz.
Description: Clear Embossed Throwaway
Date Circa.: 1960's
Value $10

 # 506
Size: 12 oz.
Description: Convention Bottle
Date Circa.: 1970's
Value $65

 # 507
Size: 12 oz.
Description: Gold dip
with wood stand
Date 1959
Value $65

84

Cans

 # 508
Size: 12 oz.
Description: Cone Top
Date Circa.: 1940's
Value $200

 # 509
Size: 12 oz.
Description: Cone Top
Date Circa.: 1940's
Value $165

 # 510
Size: 12 oz.
Description: Cont Top
Date Circa.: 1950's
Value $120

 # 511
Size: 12 oz.
Description: Flat Top
Date Circa.: 1950's
Value $20

 # 512
Size: 7 oz.
Description: Pull Tab
Date Circa.: 1960's
Value $5

 # 513
Size: 12 oz.
Description: Tab Top
Date Circa.: 1960's
Value $15

 # 514
Size: 5 1/2 oz.
Description: Tab Top
Date Circa.: 1970's
Value $5

 # 515
Size: 8 oz.
Description: Tab Top
Date Circa.: 1970's
Value $5

 # 516
Size: 1/2 Litre
Description: Resealable Aluminum
Date Circa.: 1970's
Value $5

Toys and Games

 # 517
Size: 10" x 9"
Description: Wood and Metal Pulltoy
Date Circa.: 1940's
Value $275

 # 518
Description: Refreshment stand wagon with original box
Date Circa.: 1940's
Value $200

 # 519
Size: 7" x 9" x 3"
Description: Metal Toy Dispenser Bank
Date Circa.: 1950's
Value $200

 # 520
Description: Refreshment stand wagon (Umbrella missing)
Date Circa.: 1940's
Value $150

 # 522
Size: 3" High
Description: Plastic Whistle
Date Circa.: 1950's
Value $50

 # 521
Size: 5" x 3"
Description: Cardboard Pocket Baseball Game
Date Circa.: 1930's
Value $150

 # 523
Description: Plastic Fireman's Hat
Date Circa.: 1950's
Value $35

Toys and Games

 # 524
Size: 20"
Description: Stuffed Santa Figure
Date Circa.: 1970's
Value $30

 # 525
Size: 18"
Description: Stuffed Elf Figure
Date Circa.: 1970's
Value $25

 # 526
Description: Plastic Toy Dispenser
Date Circa.: 1950's
Value $45

 # 527
Size: 12" x 10"
Description: Cardboard Airplane
Date Circa.: 1970's
Value $10

 # 528
Size: 6" x 6"
Description: Sand Pail
Date Circa.: 1970's
Value $10

 # 529
Size: 13" High
Description: Battery Operated Bear
Date Circa.: 1950's
Value $40

 # 530
Size: 3" Dia.
Description: Rubber Ball
Date Circa.: 1960's
Value $10

 # 531
Size: 12" x 12" x 6"
Description: Plastic Toy Dispenser
Date Circa.: 1970's
Value $10

 # 532
Size: 1" Dia.
Description: Cardboard Bingo Markers
Date Circa.: 1930's
Value $5 each

Toy Trucks and Cars

 # 533
Size: 24"
Description: Wooden Truck - Rubber Wheels
Date Circa.: 1930's
Value $350

 # 534
Size: 6"
Description: Metal (Yellow)
Date Circa.: 1940's
Value $120

 # 535
Size: 5"
Description: Tin Fashion
Date Circa.: 1930's
Value $110

 # 536
Size: 6"
Description: Metal
Date Circa.: 1940's
Value $110

 # 537
Size: 11"
Description: Tin Friction Car
Date Circa.: 1960's
Value $100

 # 538
Size: 8"
Description: Plastic Truck with Box by Marx
Date Circa.: 1940's
Value $110

 # 539
Size: 16"
Description: Tin
Date Circa.: 1950's
Value $125

Toy Trucks and Cars

 # 540
Size: 8"
Description: Plastic (Incomplete)
Date Circa.: 1940's
Value $90

 # 541
Size: 8"
Description: Tin Truck with box
Date Circa.: 1950's
Value $60

 # 542
Size: 20"
Description: Tin Truck
Date Circa.: 1950's
Value $60

 # 543
Size: 12"
Description: Tin Friction with original box
Date Circa.: 1950's
Value $85

 # 544
Size: 24"
Description: Radio Controlled
Date Circa.: 1970's
Value $100

 # 545
Size: 12"
Description: Buddy L.
Date Circa.: 1960's
Value $40

 # 546
Size: 5"
Description: Tin Friction
Date Circa.: 1950's
Value $30

Toy Trucks and Cars

 # 547
Size: 2"
Description: Metal
Date Circa.: 1960's
Value $45

 # 548
Size: 27"
Description: Plastic
Date Recent
Value $20

 # 549
Size: 8"
Description: Tonka Truck
Date Circa.: 1970's
Value $20

 # 550
Size: 24"
Description: ERTL Semi
Date Recent
Value $15

 # 551
Description: Buddy L 3 piece set
Date Circa.: 1970's
Value $15

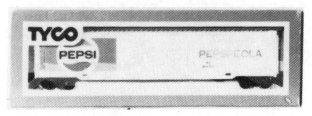

 # 552
Size: 8"
Description: Tyco Train Car
Date Circa.: 1970's
Value $15

 # 553
Size: 8"
Description: Mexican Plastic
Date Recent
Value $15

Toy Trucks and Cars

 # 554
Size: 12"
Description: Mexican Plastic
Date Recent
Value $15

 # 555
Size: 11"
Description: ERTL Semi
Date Recent
Value $10

 # 556
Size: 3"
Description: Metal Matchbox Truck
Date Circa.: 1970's
Value $5

 # 557
Size: 2"
Description: Metal Matchbox Truck
Date Circa.: 1970's
Value $5

 # 558
Size: 2"
Description: Metal Matchbox Truck
Date Circa.: 1970's
Value $5

 # 559
Size: 2"
Description: Metal Matchbox Van
Date Circa.: 1970's
Value $5

 # 560
Size: 4"
Description: Plastic and Tin
Date Circa.: 1960's
Value $10

Miniatures

 # 561
Size: 9" x 6" x 5"
Description: Cooler with original box
Date Circa.: 1940's
Value $1200

 # 562
Size: 3" x 6 3/4"
Description: Plastic Vending Machine Bank
Date Circa.: 1940's
Value $95 Bank only

 # 563
Size: 3" x 6 3/4"
Description: Plastic Machine Bank with box
Date Circa.: 1940's
Value $125 bank and box

 # 564
Size: 3" x 4" x 3"
Description: Composition Bank
Date Circa.: 1940's
Value $90

Miniatures

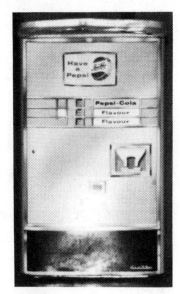

 # 565
Size: 3" x 5" x 2"
Description: Tin Machine Bank
Date Circa.: 1950's
Value $35

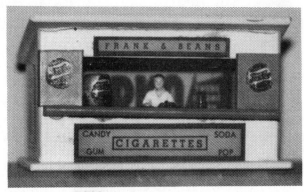

 # 566
Size: 6" x 3" x 3"
Description: Toy Refreshment Stand
Date Circa.: 1940's
Value $125

 # 567
Size: 5" x 4"
Description: Tin Billboard for Train Set
Date Circa.: 1940's
Value $85

 # 568
Size: 8" High
Description: Lamp
Date Circa.: 1940's
Value $300

Miniatures

 # 569
Size: 4"
Description: Paper label salt and pepper
Date Circa.: 1930's
Value $55 set

 # 570
Size: 3"
Description: Paper label salt and pepper
Date Circa.: 1940's
Value $40 set

 # 571
Size: 4"
Description: Glass salt and pepper
Date Circa.: 1960's
Value $5 set

 # 572
Size: 4"
Description: Paper label salt and pepper with original box
Date Circa.: 1930's
Value $100

 # 573
Size: 2" x 1"
Description: Miniature 6 pack / plastic bottles
Date Circa.: 1945's
Value $100

 # 574
Description: Cardboard 6-pack with glass bottles
Date Circa.: 1950's
Value $55

Smoking Paraphenalia

4" x 4"
ption: Glass Ashtray with Decal
Circa.: 1930's
$65

 # 576
Size: 4" x 4"
Description: Glass Ashtray
Date Circa.: 1960's
Value $15

 # 577
Size: 5" x 4"
Description: Glass Ashtray
Date 1963
Value $30

 # 578
Size: 5" x 4"
Description: Glass Ashtray
Date Circa.: 1960's
Value $30

9
: 2"
cription: Metal Lighter with box
e Circa.: 1940's
e $75 with box

 # 580
Size: 2"
Description: Bottle Lighter
Date Circa.: 1930's
Value $50

 # 581
Size: 2"
Description: Bottle Lighter
Date Circa.: 1940's
Value $40

 # 582
Size: 2"
Description: Evervess Bottle Lighter
Date Circa.: 1950's
Value $40

 # 583
Size: 3"
Description: Enameled
Bottle Cap Lighter
Date Circa.: 1940's
Value $75

 # 584
Size: 2"
Description: Scripto Lighter
Date Circa.: 1950's
Value $30

 # 585
Size: 2"
Description: Zippo Lighter
with enameled bottle cap
Date Circa.: 1950
Value $45

 # 586
Size: 2" x 3"
Description: Lighter
Date Circa.: 1960's
Value $15

 # 587
Size: 3"
Description: Scripto Lighter
Date Circa.: 1960's
Value $15

 # 588
Size: 1" x 2"
Description: Lighter
Date Circa.: 1960's
Value $10

9
2"
ription: Plastic Bottle Shaped Lighter
Circa.: 1950's
e $15

 # 590
Size: 12 oz.
Description: Can Lighter
Date Circa.: 1950's
Value $20

 # 591
Size: 2"
Description: Metal Lighter
Date Circa.: 1960's
Value $20

 # 592
Size: 3" x 1"
Description: Butane Lighter
Date Circa.: 1960's
Value $15

Smoking Paraphenalia

 # 593
Description: Matchbook
Date Circa.: 1940's
Value $10

 # 594
Description: Matchbook
Date Circa.: 1940's
Value $10

 # 595
Description: Matchbook
Date Circa.: 1940's
Value $10

 # 596
Description: Matchbook
Date Circa.: 1930's
Value $15

 # 597
Description: Matchbo
Date Circa.: 1930's
Value $15

 # 598
Description: Matchbook
Date Circa.: 1930's
Value $15

 # 599
Description: Matchbook
Date Circa.: 1930's
Value $15

 # 600
Description: Matchbook
Date Circa.: 1940's
Value $10

 # 601
Description: Matchbook
Date Circa.: 1940's
Value $10

 # 602
Description: Matchbook
Date Circa.: 1940's
Value $20

Smoking Paraphenalia

 # 603
Description: Matchbook
Date Circa.: 1940's
Value $20

 # 604
Description: Matchbook
Date Circa.: 1940's
Value $20

 # 605
Description: Matchbook
Date Circa.: 1930's
Value $10

 # 606
Description: Matchbook Die Cut
Date Circa.: 1940's
Value $30

 # 607
Description: Matchbook
Date Circa.: 1950's
Value $15

 # 608
Description: Matchbook
Date Circa.: 1950's
Value $5

 # 609
Description: Matchbook
Date Circa.: 1950's
Value $5

 # 610
Description: Matchbook
Date Circa.: 1950's
Value $5

Smoking Paraphenalia

 # 611
Description: Matchbook
Date Circa.: 1950's
Value $5

 # 612
Description: Matchbook
Date Circa.: 1960's
Value $5

 # 613
Description: Matchbook
Date Circa.: 1960's
Value $5

 # 614
Description: Matchbook
Date Circa.: 1970's
Value $5

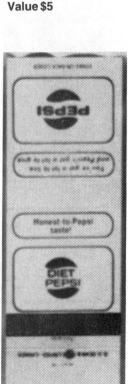

 # 615
Description: Matchbook
Date Circa.: 1970's
Value $5

 # 616
Description: Matchbook
Date Circa.: 1970's
Value $5

 # 617
Description: Matchbook
Date Circa.: 1970's
Value $5

 # 618
Description: Matchbook
Date Circa.: 1970's
Value $5

Playing Cards

  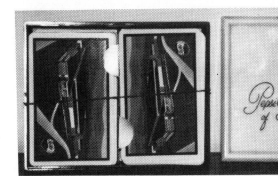

 # 619
Description: Bottle Cap
Date Circa.: 1940's
Value per deck $85

 # 620
Description: Bottle Cap "Drink"
Date Circa.: 1940's
Value $85

 # 621
Description: Double Deck Cincinnati, Bottling Plant
Date Circa.: 1950's
Value $100

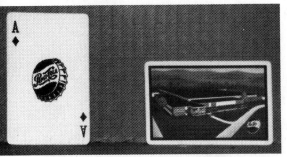  

 # 622
Description: Cincinnati Botting Plant
Date Circa.: 1950's
Value per deck $50

 # 623
Description: Pepsi Cola
Date Circa.: 1940's
Value $85

 # 624
Description: Drink Pepsi Cola
Date Circa.: 1940's
Value $85

 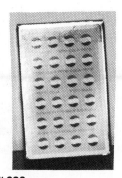 

#625
Description: Pete Rose
Date Circa.: 1970's
Value $50

 # 626
Description: Multi Bottle Caps
Date Circa.: 1950's
Value $50

 # 627
Description: Bottle Cap Red and white
Date Circa.: 1950's
Value $50

Pens and Pencils

 # 628
Size: 6"
Description: Fountain pen with original box
Date Circa.: 1930's
Value $95

 # 634
Size: 10" x 10"
Description: Softball Championship Desk Set (Pen not origi
Date 1941
Value $225

 # 629
Size: 6"
Description: Fountain Pen
Date Circa.: 1930's
Value $65

 # 630
Size: 6"
Description: Mechanical Pencil
Date Circa.: 1940's
Value $65

 # 635
Size: 2" x 3"
Description: Sample Desk Pen Holder
Date Circa.: 1950's
Value $45

 # 631
Size: 7"
Description: Mechanical Pencil
Date Circa.: 1940's
Value $75

 # 636
Size: 9"
Description: Wooden Pencil
Date Circa.: 1960's
Value $5

 # 632
Size: 6"
Description: Mechanical Pencil
Date Circa.: 1950's
Value $20

 # 637
Size: 6"
Description: Mechanical Pencil
Date Circa.: 1950's
Value $35

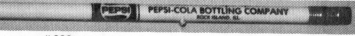

 # 633
Size: 9"
Description: Wooden Pencil Rock Island, Inc.
Date Circa.: 1960's
Value $5

Openers

 # 638
Size: 2" x 4"
Description: Wall Type
Date Circa.: 1910's
Value $100

 # 639
Size: 5" High
Description: Cast Iron Wall Type
Date Circa.: 1930's
Value $65

 # 640
Size: 2" x 3"
Description: Lithographed Wall Type
Date Circa.: 1930's
Value $75

 # 641
Size: 6"
Description: Heavy Brass
Date Circa.: 1950's
Value $85

 # 642
Size: 6"
Description: Heavy Brass
Date Circa.: 1940's
Value $75

 # 643
Size: 4"
Description: Wooden Handle
Date Circa.: 1920's
Value $80

Openers

 # 644
Size: 3"
Description: Flat
Date Circa.: 1910's
Value $80

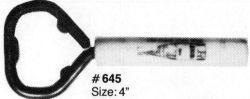

 # 645
Size: 4"
Description: Plastic Handle with bottle
Date Circa.: 1940's
Value $55

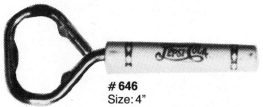

 # 646
Size: 4"
Description: Plastic Handle
Date Circa.: 1940's
Value $45

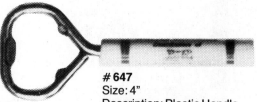

 # 647
Size: 4"
Description: Plastic Handle
Date Circa.: 1940's
Value $45

 # 648
Size: 4"
Description: 3-D
Date Circa.: 1930's
Value $45

 # 649
Size: 5"
Description: Flat
Date Circa.: 1940's
Value $40

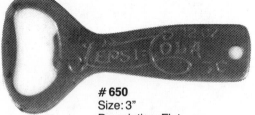

 # 650
Size: 3"
Description: Flat
Date Circa.: 1930's
Value $40

 # 651
Size: 4"
Description: 3-D
Date Circa.: 1930's
Value $30

 # 652
Size: 4"
Description: Over The Top
Date Circa.: 1930's
Value $30

Openers

 # 653
Size: 3"
Description: Flat Figural
Date Circa.: 1930's
Value $35

 # 654
Size: 3"
Description: Flat Figural
Date Circa.: 1930's
Value $35

 # 655
Size: 4"
Description: Lithographed Tin
Date Circa.: 1930's
Value $20

 # 656
Size: 3"
Description: Figural
Date Circa.: 1930's
Value $15

 # 657
Size: 5"
Description: Flat
Date Circa.: 1950's
Value $15

 # 658
Size: 5"
Description: Flat
Date Circa.: 1950's
Value $15

 # 659
Size: 5"
Description: Flat
Date Circa.: 1950's
Value $15

 # 660
Size: 5"
Description: Flat
Date Circa.: 1950's
Value $15

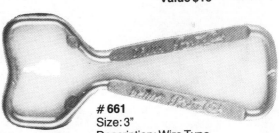

 # 661
Size: 3"
Description: Wire Type
Date Circa.: 1950's
Value $5

 # 662
Size: 4"
Description: Punch Type
Date Circa.: 1950's
Value $5

 # 663
Size: 4"
Description: Punch Type
Date Circa.: 1950's
Value $5

 # 664
Size: 6"
Description: Plastic Handle Memphis, Tenn.
Date Circa.: 1950's
Value $15

 # 665
Size: 3" x 2"
Description: Cast-Iron Starr X
Date Circa.: 1950's
Value $15

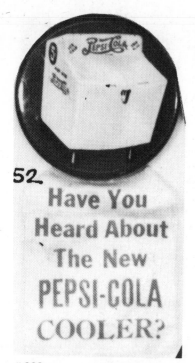

52

Have You Heard About The New PEPSI-COLA COOLER?

 # 666
Size: 3"
Description: Celluloid with Ribbon
Date Circa.: 1940's
Value $90

 # 667
Size: 2 1/2" Dia.
Description: Celluloid with Tin
Date Circa.: 1940's
Value $55

 # 668
Size: 2 3/4" Diameter
Description: Convention Button with original r
Date Circa.: 1940's
Value $35

 # 669
Size: 2 1/2" Dia.
Description: Celluloid with Tin
Date Circa.: 1950's
Value $30

 # 670
Size: 2 1/2" Dia.
Description: Celluloid with Tin
Date Circa.: 1940's
Value $35

 # 671
Size: 2 1/2" Dia.
Description: Celluloid with Tin
Date Circa.: 1950's
Value $30

 # 672
Size: 1"
Description: Celluloid with Tin
Date Circa.: 1930's
Value $35

 # 673
Size: 2 1/2" Dia.
Description: Celluloid with Tin (Yellow)
Date Circa.: 1930's
Value $35

 # 674
Size: 2 1/2" Dia.
Description: Tin/Celluloid
Date Circa.: 1930's
Value $35

Pinbacks

 # 675
Size: 2 1/2" Dia.
Description: Tin/Celluloid
Date Circa.: 1930's
Value $50

 # 676
Size: 2 1/2" Dia.
Description: Tin/Celluloid
Date Circa.: 1940's
Value $50

 # 677
Size: 2 1/2" x 2 1/2"
Description: Celluloid/Tin
Date Circa.: 1950's
Value $25

 # 678
Size: 2 1/2" Dia.
Description: Celluloid/Tin
Date Circa.: 1950's
Value $25

 # 679
Size: 2"
Description: Celluloid
Date Circa.: 1950's
Value $20

 # 680
Size: 2"
Description: Celluloid
Date Circa.: 1950's
Value $15

 # 681
Size: 2 1/2" Dia.
Description: Celluloid/Tin
Date Circa.: 1970's
Value $5

 # 682
Size: 2 1/2" Dia.
Description: Celluloid/Tin
Date Circa.: 1970's
Value $5

 # 683
Size: 3" x 2"
Description: Madison, IN. Regatta
Date 1967
Value $15

 # 684
Size: 2 1/2" Dia.
Description: Madison, IN Regatta
Date 1966
Value $15

Calendars

 # 685
Size: 14" x 20"
Description: Embossed cardboard die cut with 12 month pad
Date 1939
Value $425

 # 686
Size: 18" x 26"
Description: Cardboard with 12 month pad Petty Art
Date 1941
Value $400

 # 687
Size: 16" x 21"
Description: 12 Sheet
Date 1941
Value $50

 # 688
Description: Cardboard with 12 month pad
Date 1941
Value $165

Calendars

 # 689
Size: 16" x 21"
Description: 12 sheet
Date 1942
Value $50

 # 690
Size: 16" x 21"
Description: 12 sheet
Date 1943
Value $50

 # 691
Size: 7" x 4"
Description: Pocket Size Blue and White
Date 1943
Value $40

 # 692
Size: 15" x 21"
Description: 12 sheet
Date 1944
Value $50

 # 693
Size: 16" x 21"
Description: 12 sheet
Date 1945
Value $50

Calendars

 # 694
Size: 16" x 21"
Description: 12 sheet
Date 1946
Value $50

 # 695
Size: 15" x 20"
Description: 12 sheet
Date 1947
Value $50

 # 696
Size: 16" x 21"
Description: 12 sheet
Date 1948
Value $75

 # 697
Size: 16" x 21"
Description: 12 sheet
Date 1949
Value $100

 # 698
Size: 13" x 22"
Description: 6 sheet
Date 1950
Value $90

Calendars

 # 699
Size: 12" x 9"
Description: Cardboard Easel Back 12 sheet
Date 1955
Value $75

 # 700
Size: 9" x 15"
Description: Cardboard (No pad)
Date 1971
Value $10

 # 701
Size: 9" x 13"
Description: Cardboard (No pad)
Date 1973
Value $10

 # 702
Size: 8" x 12"
Description: Metal Perpetual
Date Recent
Value $10

 # 703
Size: 9" x 4"
Date Circa.: 1900's
Value $225

 # 704
Size: 9" x 4"
Date Circa.: 1900's
Value $225

 # 705
Size: 9" x 4"
Date Circa.: 1900's
Value $225

 # 706
Size: 9 1/2" x 4"
Description: Pink Background
Date Circa.: 1910-1915
Value $110

Blotters

 # 707
Size: 7" x 4"
Description: Navy Wave
Date Circa.: 1940's
Value $125

 # 708
Size: 7" x 4"
Description: Haden Haden Artwork
Date Circa.: 1940's
Value $95

 # 709
Size: 9" x 4"
Description: Pepsi & Pete
Date Circa.: 1930's
Value $80

 # 710
Size: 7 1/4" x 3 3/4"
Description: Red, White and Blue
Date Circa.: 1930's
Value $60

#711
Size: 8" x 12"
Description: Cardboard with wooden handle. Full colors
with calendar on reverse.
Date 1912-1913
Value $1500

Fans

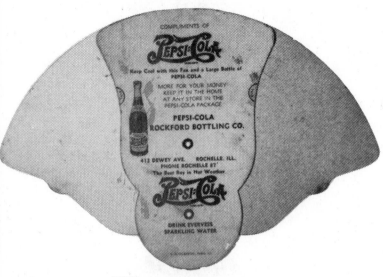

 # 712
Size: 12" x 6"
Description: Cardboard Fold-out
Date Circa.: 1930's
Value $100

 # 713
Size: 8" x 12"
Description: Cardboard with wicker handle
Date Circa.: 1930's
Value $120

 # 714
Size: 8" x 12"
Description: Cardboard with wood handle,
    (shows front and back).
Date Circa.: 1930's
Value $65

Jewelry

 # 715
Size: 4" x 2"
Description: Enameled Belt Buckle
Date Circa.: 1940's
Value $100

 # 716
Size: 4" x 2"
Description: Enameled Belt Buckler
Date Circa.: 1950's
Value $35

 # 717
Size: 1" Dia.
Description: Charm
Date Circa.: 1950's
Value $40

 # 718
Size: 1" Dia.
Description: Enameled Charm
Date Circa.: 1940's
Value $100

 # 719
Size: 2" Dia.
Description: Safety Award Key Chain
Date Circa.: 1950's
Value $20

 # 720
Size: 3" x 3"
Description: Compact with enameled bottle cap
Date Circa.: 1950's
Value $120

 # 721
Size: 1" Dia.
Description: Uniform Button
Date Circa.: 1950's
Value $10 each

Jewelry

 # 722
Size: 2" x 2"
Description: Watch FOB Embossed
Date Circa.: 1900's
Value $250

 # 724
Size: 2" x 2"
Description: Watch FOB Embossed
Date Circa.: 1900's
Value $225

 # 723
Size: 2" x 2"
Description: Watch FOB Enameled Insert
Date Circa.: 1900's
Value $225

 # 725
Size: 1" x 2"
Description: Watch FOB Embossed
Date Circa.: 1900's
Value $100

 # 726
Size: 2" x 1"
Description: Watch FOB Enameled
Date Circa.: 1960's
Value $45

 # 727
Size: 1" x 2"
Description: Softball Pin
Date Circa.: 1940's
Value $75

 # 728
Size: 1"
Description: Plastic Stickpin
Date Circa.: 1940's
Value $100

 # 729
Size: 3"
Description: Stickpin with Enameled Bottle Cap
Date Circa.: 1950's
Value $100

Uniform Patches

 # 730
Size: 10" x 5"
Description: Cloth
Date Circa.: 1930's
Value $95

 # 731
Size: 10" x 5"
Description: Cloth
Date Circa.: 1930's
Value $85

 # 732
Size: 7" Dia.
Description: Cloth
Date Circa.: 1940's
Value $60

 # 733
Size: 7" Dia.
Description: Cloth
Date Circa.: 1950's
Value $35

 # 734
Size: 7" Dia.
Description: Cloth yellow background
Date Circa.: 1950's
Value $35

 # 735
Size: 6" Dia.
Description: Cloth
Date Circa.: 1960's
Value $25

Uniform Patches

 # 736
Size: 6" Dia.
Description: Cloth
Date Circa.: 1960's
Value $25

 # 737
Size: 7" Dia.
Description: Arabic
Date Circa.: 1950's
Value $25

 # 738
Size: 7" Dia.
Description: Mexican
Date Circa.: 1950's
Value $25

 # 739
Size: 3" Dia.
Description: Cloth
Date Circa.: 1950's
Value $20

 # 740
Description: Cloth Patch on Original Jacket
Date Circa.: 1960's
Value $10

 # 741
Size: 12"
Description: Wood Ruler
Date Circa.: 1930's
Value $50

 # 742
Size: 12"
Description: Wood Ruler
Date Circa.: 1930's
Value $50

 # 743
Size: 12"
Description: Wooden Ruler
Date Circa.: 1940's
Value $40

 # 744
Size: 12"
Description: Tin Ruler
Date Circa.: 1950's
Value $25

 # 745
Size: 12"
Description: Tin Ruler
Date Circa.: 1960's
Value $15

 # 746
Size: 12"
Description: Metal Charlotte N.C. Ruler
Date Circa.: 1970's
Value $10

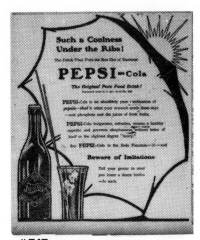

 # 747
Size: 11" x 14"
Description: B.W. Newspaper Ad
Date 1907
Value $40

 # 748
Size: 11" x 14"
Description: B.W. Newspaper Ad
Date 1907
Value $40

 # 749
Size: 11" x 14"
Description: B.W. Newspaper Ad
Date 1907
Value $45

 # 750
Size: 11" x 14"
Description: Black and white
Date 1907
Value $45

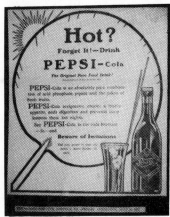

 # 751
Size: 11" x 14"
Description: Black and white
Date 1907
Value $40

 # 752
Size: 11" x 14"
Description: Black and white
Date 1907
Value $45

 # 753
Size: 11" x 14"
Description: Black and white
Date 1907
Value $40

 # 754
Size: 11" x 14"
Description: Color
Date Circa.: 1930's
Value $15

 # 755
Size: 11" x 14"
Description: Color
Date Circa.: 1930's
Value $15

 # 756
Size: 11" x 14"
Description: Color
Date Circa.: 1930's
Value $15

 # 757
Size: 11" x 14"
Description: Color
Date Circa.: 1930's
Value $15

 # 758
Size: 11" x 14"
Description: Color
Date Circa.: 1930's
Value $15

Magazine Ads

 # 759
Size: 11" x 7"
Description: Color
Date Circa.: 1930's
Value $45

 # 760
Size: 11" x 14"
Description: Color
Date Circa.: 1930's
Value $15

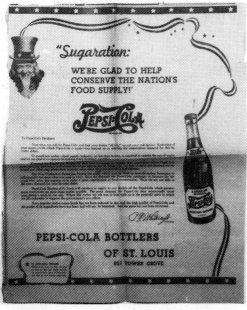

 # 761
Size: 11" x 14"
Description: Black and white Newspaper Ad
Date Circa.: 1940's
Value $40

 # 762
Size: 11" x 14"
Description: Color
Date Circa.: 1930's
Value $15

 # 763
Size: 11" x 14"
Description: Color
Date Circa.: 1930's
Value $15

 # 764
Size: 11" x 14"
Description: Pepsi Truck
Date Circa.: 1940's
Value $25

 # 765
Size: 6" x 14"
Description: Black and white
Date Circa.: 1940's
Value $15

 # 766
Size: 11" x 14"
Description: Black and white
Date Circa.: 1940's
Value $15

 # 767
Size: 14" x 11"
Description: Black and white
Date Circa.: 1940's
Value $15

 # 768
Size: 14" x 11"
Description: Black and white
Date Circa.: 1940's
Value $15

 # 769
Size: 11" x 14"
Description: Black and white
Date Circa.: 1940's
Value $15

 # 770
Size: 11" x 14"
Description: Black and white
Date Circa.: 1940's
Value $15

Magazine Ads

 # 771
Size: 11" x 14"
Description: Color
Date Circa.: 1950's
Value $15

 # 772
Size: 11" x 14"
Description: Color
Date Circa.: 1950's
Value $15

 # 773
Size: 11" x 14"
Description: Color
Date Circa.: 1950's
Value $10

 # 774
Size: 11" x 14"
Description: Color
Date Circa.: 1950's
Value $10

 # 775
Size: 11" x 14"
Description: Color
Date Circa.: 1950's
Value $10

 # 776
Size: 11" x 14"
Description: Color
Date Circa.: 1950's
Value $10

Magazine Ads

 # 777
Size: 11" x 14"
Description: Color
Date Circa.: 1950's
Value $10

 # 778
Size: 11" x 14"
Description: Color
Date Circa.: 1950's
Value $10

 # 779
Size: 11" x 14"
Description: Color
Date Circa.: 1950's
Value $10

 # 780
Size: 11" x 14"
Description: Color
Date Circa.: 1950's
Value $10

 # 781
Size: 11" x 14"
Description: Color
Date Circa.: 1950's
Value $10

 # 782
Size: 11" x 14"
Description: Color
Date Circa.: 1950's
Value $10

Notebooks

 # 783
Size: 3" x 5"
Date Circa.: 1910's
Value $75

 # 784
Size: 3" x 6"
Date Circa.: 1910's
Value $45

 # 785
Size: 3" x 5"
Date Circa.: 1910's
Value $40

 # 786
Size: 3" x 5"
Date Circa.: 1910's
Value $40

 # 787
Size: 3" x 5"
Date Circa.: 1910's
Value $40

 # 788
Size: 3" x 5"
Date Circa.: 1910's
Value $40

 # 789
Size: 4" x 6"
Description: From the Desk of Joan Crawford
Date Circa.: 1970's
Value $20

Brochures

 # 790
Size: 9" x 12"
Description: Booklet with envelope
Date 1938
Value $110

 # 791
Size: 9" x 12"
Description: Booklet
Date Circa.: 1939
Value $85

 # 792
Size: 8 1/2" x 11"
Description: Sales Catalog
Date 1940
Value $50

 # 793
Size: 8 1/2" x 11"
Description: Drum Cooler Flyer
Date Circa.: 1930's
Value $25

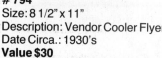

 # 794
Size: 8 1/2" x 11"
Description: Vendor Cooler Flyer
Date Circa.: 1930's
Value $30

 # 795
Size: 8 1/2" x 11"
Description: Athletic Sales Catalog
Date 1950
Value $25

 # 796
Size: 8 1/2" x 11"
Description: Sign Flyer
Date Circa.: 1930's
Value $25

Brochures

 # 797
Size: 8 1/2" x 11"
Description: Utility Cooler Flyer
Date Circa.: 1930's
Value $25

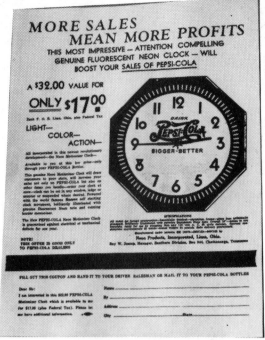

 # 798
Size: 8 1/2" x 11"
Description: Clock Flyer
Date Circa.: 1930's
Value $25

 # 799
Size: 8 1/2" x 11"
Description: Radio Copy
Date 1938
Value $35

 # 801
Size: 11" x 8 1/2"
Description: Sales Booklet
Date Circa.: 1940's
Value $40

 # 800
Size: 8 1/2" x 11"
Description: Pepsi World Mag.
Date 1947
Value $40

 # 802
Size: 8" x 11"
Description: Sales Training Program
Date 1940
Value $35

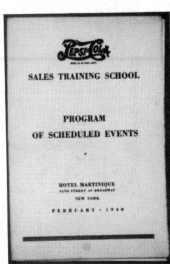

Letterheads, Invoices & Envelopes

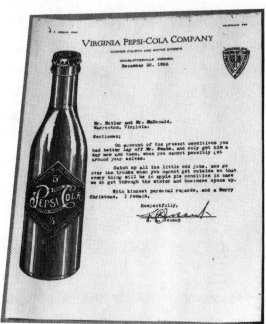

 # 803
Size: 8 1/2" x 11"
Description: Letterhead, Charlottesville, VA.
Date Circa.: 1900's
Value $85

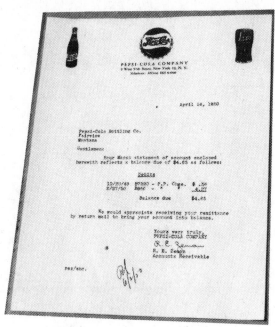

 # 804
Size: 8 1/2" x 11"
Description: Letterhead, New York
Date 1950
Value $15

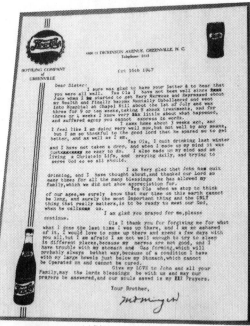

 # 805
Size: 8 1/2" x 11"
Description: Letterhead, Greenville, N.C.
Date 1947
Value $25

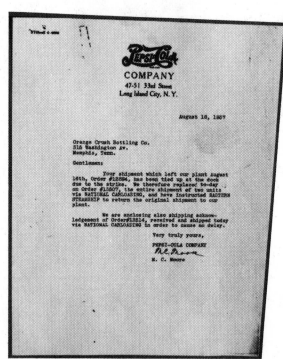

 # 806
Size: 8 1/2" x 11"
Description: Letterhead, Long Island
Date 1935
Value $20

Letterheads, Invoices & Envelopes

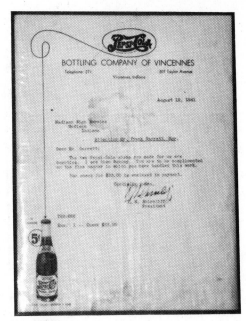

 # 807
Size: 8 1/2" x 11"
Description: Letterhead, Vincinnes, IN
Date 1941
Value $20

 # 808
Size: 8 1/2" x 6"
Description: Letterhead, Jackson, Tenn.
Date Circa.: 1930's
Value $20

 # 809
Size: 8 1/2" x 11"
Description: Letterhead, Jackson, Tenn.
Date Circa.: 1950's
Value $15

 # 810
Size: 8 1/2" x 6"
Description: Letterhead, Jackson, Tenn.
Date Circa.: 1950's
Value $10

Letterheads, Invoices & Envelopes

 # 811
Size: 12" x 4"
Description: Weldon, N.C. In.
Date 1915
Value $20

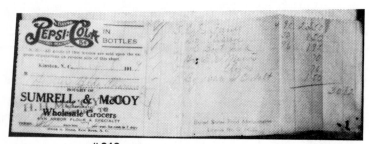

 # 812
Size: 12" x 14"
Description: Sumrell & McCoy Invoice
Date 1919
Value $20

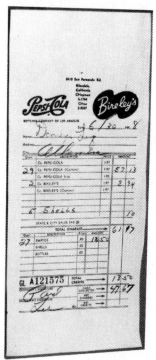

 # 813
Size: 4" x 8"
Description: Invoice, Los Angeles, CA.
Date 1958
Value $10

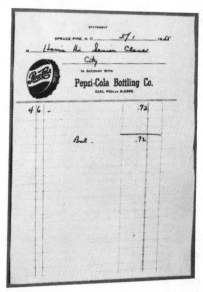

 # 814
Size: 6" x 8"
Description: Invoice, Spruce Pine, N.C.
Date 1955
Value $10

 # 815
Size: 10" x 4"
Description: Invoice Weldon, N.C.
Date 1918
Value $15

Letterheads, Invoices & Envelopes

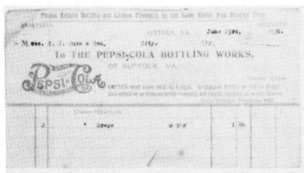

 # 816
Size: 12" x 6"
Description: Suffolk, Virginia Invoice
Date 1920
Value $20

 # 817
Size: 6"
Description: Envelope, Charlottesville, VA.
Date Circa.: 1900's
Value $25

 # 818
Size: 8 1/2"
Description: Envelope Shelbyville, Tenn.
Date 1948
Value $15

 # 819
Size: 8 1/2"
Description: Envelope, Vincinnes, IN
Date 1941
Value $15

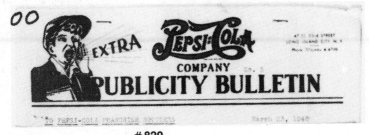

 # 820
Size: 8 1/2" x 11"
Description: Publicity Bulletin
Date Circa.: 1930's
Value $25

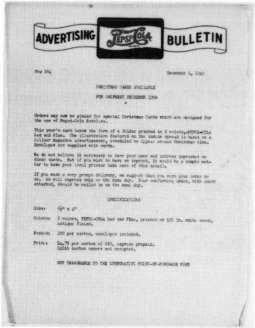

 # 821
Size: 8 1/2" x 11"
Description: Advertising Bulletin
Date Circa.: 1940's
Value $20

 # 822
Size: 8 1/2" x 11"
Description: Advertising Bulletin
Date 1944
Value $20

 # 823
Size: 8" x 4"
Description: Check, Jackson, Tenn.
Date 1954
Value $5

 # 824
Size: 8" x 4"
Description: Check, Jackson, Tenn.
Date 1949
Value $10

 # 825
Size: 8" x 4"
Description: Check Shelbyville, Tenn.
Date 1946
Value $10

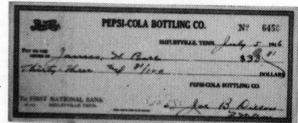

Miscellaneous

 # 826
Size: 3" x 2"
Description: Pocket Mirror Charlotte, N.C.
Date Circa.: 1910's
Value $750

 # 827
Size: 6"
Description: Shoe Brush
Date Circa.: 1900's
Value $135

 # 828
Size: 4" Dia.
Description: Street Safety Marker
Date Circa.: 1920's
Value $145

 # 829
Size: 10" x 16"
Description: Wooden Knife Rack with marked knives
Date Circa.: 1960's
Value $75

 # 830
Size: 3" x 5"
Description: Bottle Bag
Date Circa.: 1930's
Value $40

 # 831
Size: 6" x 6" x 3"
Description: Glass Bookends
Date Circa.: 1960's
Value $35

Miscellaneous

 # 833
Size: 71" Dia.
Description: Vendors Umbrella
Date Circa.: 1950's
Value $80

 # 832
Description: Sample Vendors Cart
Date Circa.: 1950's
Value $135

 # 834
Description: Chair
Date Circa.: 1950's
Value $150

 # 835
Size: 7" x 11" x 5"
Description: Chackware Bottle holder (Not Original Bottle)
Date Circa.: 1940's
Value $175

Miscellaneous

 # 836
Size: 24" x 30"
Description: Mary Poppins Kite
Date Circa.: 1960's
Value $90

 # 837
Description: Bridge Score Sheet
Date Circa.: 1940's
Value $15

 # 838
Description: First Aid Kit
Date Circa.: 1970's
Value $10

 # 839
Size: 11" Dia. 9" High
Description: Tin Cake Carrier
Date Circa.: 1960's
Value $35

 # 840
Description: Sewing Kit
Date Circa.: 1950's
Value $15

 # 841
Description: Houston Colts Baseball Card
Date Circa.: 1960's
Value $10 ea.

 # 842
Description: Artist Proof of Tin Sign
Date Circa.: 1940's
Value $30

 # 843
Description: Cloth Shirt
Date Circa.: 1960's
Value $15

 # 844
Size: 4" Dia.
Description: Glass Paperweight
Date Circa.: 1950's
Value $55

 # 845
Size: 3 pack
Description: Golf balls
Date Circa.: 1970's
Value $15

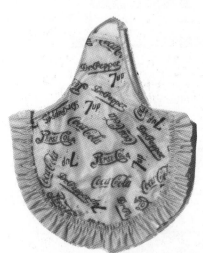

 # 846
Size: 8" x 12"
Description: Plastic Doll Apron
Date Circa.: 1940's
Value $45

 # 848
Description: Rubber Change Mat
Date Circa.: 1960's
Value $15

 # 847
Size: 9 1/2" x 7 3/4"
Description: Rubber Counter Change Mat
Date Circa.: 1960's
Value $10

 # 850
Size: 8" x 10"
Description: Plastic Change Receiver
Date Circa.: 1960's
Value $20

 # 849
Size: 8" x 10"
Description: Plastic Change Receiver
Date Circa.: 1960's
Value $15

 # 851
Size: 12" x 6"
Description: License Plate
Date 1976
Value $10

 # 852
Size: 12" x 6"
Description: License Plate Tenn.
Date 1976
Value $10

Miscellaneous

 # 853
Size: 16" x 22"
Description: Vendor's Apron
Date Circa.: 1950's
Value $40

 # 854
Size: 16" x 22"
Description: Vendor's Apron
Date Circa.: 1950's
Value $35

 # 855
Size: 16" x 22"
Description: Apron
Date Circa.: 1960's
Value $40

 # 856
Size: 4" Dia.
Description: Cardboard Coaster
Date Circa.: 1940's
Value $20

 # 857
Size: 4" Dia.
Description: Cardboard Coaster
Date Circa.: 1940's
Value $20

 # 858
Size: 4" x 4"
Description: Cardboard Coaster
Date Circa.: 1960's
Value $15

Miscellaneous

 # 859
Description: Record and Mailing Folder
Date Circa.: 1940's
Value $60

 # 860
Description: Dance Record
Date Circa.: 1960's
Value $15

 # 861
Description: Record (Both sides shown)
Date Circa.: 1940's
Value $50

 # 862
Size: 6" x 10"
Description: Fountain Menu
Date Circa.: 1940's
Value $55

 # 863
Size: 6" x 10"
Description: Fountain Menu
Date Circa.: 1940's
Value $35

 # 864
Size: 6" x 10"
Description: Fountain Menu
Date Circa.: 1940's
Value $35

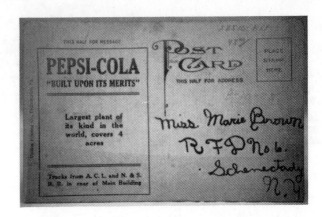

 # 865
Size: 5" x 3"
Description: Postcard, New Bern, N.C.
Date Circa.: 1910
Value $65

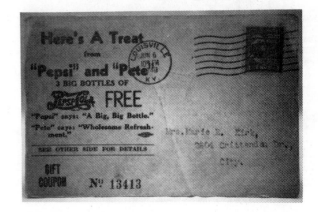

 # 866
Size: 5" x 3"
Description: Free Coupon / Postcard
Date 1940
Value $65

 # 867
Size: 5" x 3"
Description: Post Card
Date Circa.: 1950's
Value $20

 # 868
Size: 3" x 1"
Description: Free Coupon / Ticket
Date Circa.: 1940's
Value $40

Miscellaneous

 # 869
Size: 10" x 8"
Description: Photograph Greensboro, N.C.
Date Circa.: 1900's
Value $45

 # 870
Size: 7" x 5"
Description; Photograph, Norton, VA.
Date 1912
Value $50

 # 871
Size: 10" x 8"
Description: Photograph, Savannah, GA.
Date 1908
Value $70

 # 872
Size: 10" x 8"
Description: Photograph
Date Circa.: 1930's
Value $35

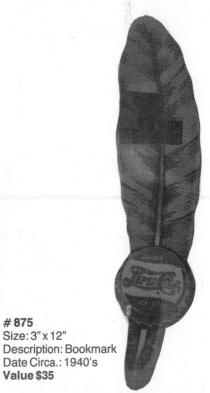

 # 873
Size: 3" x 12"
Description: Bookmark
Date Circa.: 1940's
Value $35

 # 874
Size: 3" x 12"
Description: Bookmark
Date Circa.: 1940's
Value $35

 # 875
Size: 3" x 12"
Description: Bookmark
Date Circa.: 1940's
Value $35

Miscellaneous

 # 876
 Size: 1"
Description: Bottle Cap
Date Circa.: 1920's
Value $20

 # 877
Size: 1"
Description: Brass Token, Vincinnes, IN
Date Circa.: 1900's
Value $35

 # 878
Size: 3"
Description: Pocket Knife
Date Circa.: 1930's
Value $75

 # 879
Description: Lithographed
Tin Reusable Bottle Cap
Date Circa.: 1940's
Value $35

 # 880
Size: 3/4" Dia.
Description: Celluloid Pencil Clip, Chambersburg, PA.
Date Circa.: 1940's
Value $45

 # 881
Size: 3/4" Dia.
Description: Celluloid Pencil Clip
Date Circa.: 1950's
Value $5

 # 882
Size: 1"
Description: Celluloid Bottle Capper
Date Circa.: 1950's
Value $55

 # 883
Size: 3"
Description: Plastic Stopper / Pourer
Date Circa.: 1940's
Value $20

Miscellaneous

 # 884
Size: 5" x 3"
Description: Address Book
Date Circa.: 1950's
Value $15

 # 885
Size: 2" Dia.
Description: Paper Calendar Holder
Date Circa.: 1940's
Value $25

 # 886
Size: 12" x 5"
Description: War Bond Holder
Date Circa.: 1940's
Value $70

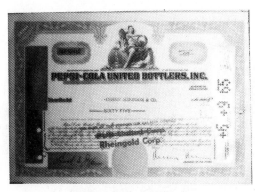

 # 887
Size: 12" x 8"
Description: Stock Certificate
Date 1965
Value $15

 # 888
Size: 2" x 3"
Description: Metal Bill Clip
Date Circa.: 1950's
Value $30

 # 889
Size: 4" x 4"
Description: Sticker
Date Circa.: 1950's
Value $15

Miscellaneous

 # 890
Size: 11" x 6"
Description: Oil Cloth Vendors Hat
Date Circa.: 1940's
Value $45

 # 891
Size: 12" x 12"
Description: Paper Visor
Date Circa.: 1950's
Value $20

 # 892
Size: 10" x 4"
Description: Paper Vendor's hat
Date Circa.: 1950's
Value $15

 # 893
Size: 10" x 4"
Description: Paper Vendor's hat
Date Circa.: 1950's
Value $10

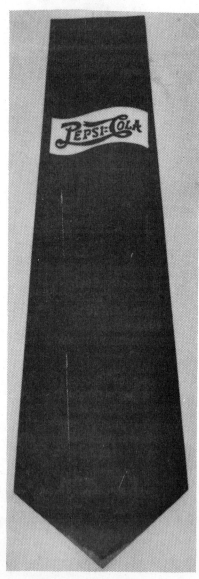

 # 894
Size: 4" Wide
Description: Cloth Necktie
Date Circa.: 1930's
Value $100

Miscellaneous

 # 895
Size: 9" x 4"
Description: Paper Vendor's hat
Date Circa.: 1950's
Value $15

 # 896
Description: Wrapping paper
Date Circa.: 1960's
Value $10

 # 897
Size: 3"
Description: Necktie
Date Circa.: 1950's
Value $50

 # 898
Size: 10" x 4"
Description: Contest Certificate
Date Circa.: 1940's
Value $25

 # 899
Size: 3" x 2"
Description: Free Coupon
Date Circa.: 1910's
Value $65

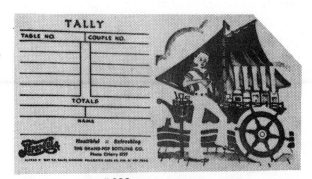

 # 900
Size: 5" x 3"
Description: Bridge Tally
Date Circa.: 1930's
Value $55

Miscellaneous

 # 901
Size: 16" Diameter
Description: Plastic Light-up Sign
Date Circa.: 1940's
Value $275

 # 902
Size: 10 oz.
Description: Pepsi & Pete Enameled Glass (2 Views)
Date Circa.: 1930's
Value $250

 # 903
Size: 26" x 21"
Description: Self Framed Cardboard Sign
Date Circa.: 1950's
Value $90

 # 904
Size: 24 Bottle
Description: Cardboard Case with Metal Rim
Date Circa.: 1940's
Value $110

 # 906
Size: 12" x 8"
Description: Plastic Light-up Sign
Date Circa.: 1960's
Value $30

 # 905
Size: 9" Diameter
Description: Tin/Cardboard Sign (Pepsi Product)
Date Circa.: 1940's
Value $65

Miscellaneous

 # 907
Size: 36 Glasses
Description: Cardboard Box for 10 oz. Glasses
Date Circa.: 1940's
Value $35

 # 908
Size: 4 Gallon Glass Jugs
Description: Cardboard Box
Date Circa.: 1960's
Value $10

 # 909
Size: 14" x 18"
Description: Plastic Light-up Clock
Date Circa.: 1970's
Value $25

Pepsi taste beats the others <u>cold</u>!

 # 910
Size: 28" x 11"
Description: Cardboard Sign
Date Circa.: 1960's
Value $15

Miscellaneous

 # 912
Size: 6" x 12"
Description: Glass over foil sign
Date Circa.: 1960's
Value $25

 # 911
Size: 13"
Description: Flat Rim Serving Tray
Date Circa.: 1970's
Value $15

 # 913
Size: 12 oz.
Description: A.C.L. Bottles (Pepsi Product)
Date Circa.: 1940's
Value $20 ea.

 # 914
Description: Plastic Tap Knob
Date Circa.: 1960's
Value $5

#916
Description: Plastic & Metal Tap Knob
Date Circa.: 1960's
Value $5

 # 915
Description: Plastic & Metal Tap Knob
Date Circa.: 1960's
Value $5